TRAIL AND CAMP-FIRE STORIES

Trail and Camp-Fire Stories

BY

JULIA M. SETON

Author of *Rhythm of the Redman,*
American Indian Arts, Pulse of the Pueblo, etc.

SETON VILLAGE PRESS
Santa Fe, New Mexico

1968

PREFACE

IT IS INDEED SELDOM—ALMOST NEVER—THAT A BOOK IS edited by the one person in the world who is wholly and adequately equipped for the job. But such is the fact in the present case.

My wife, Julia, college-bred, of high traditions, a leader of youth, experienced in expression, especially in story-telling, has listened to these same stories for more than twenty-five-years. She knows what to leave out and what to emphasize. Her knowledge of the art has enabled her to put the tales into form most acceptable to readers, realizing the places where the emphasis given by personality on the stage could not be carried into print.

In this way, she has preserved on paper the vitality that was easy on the platform or by the camp-fire, but impossible by literal record on paper.

I gladly, therefore, take this opportunity to pay tribute to a genius who in this case has consented to subordinate her gifts to those of her husband.

ERNEST THOMPSON SETON

INTRODUCTION

MANY YEARS AGO, I WAS ONE OF A LARGE AUDIENCE IN a New England woodland, having come to the meeting because I had friends among the listeners. My own interests were along other lines, and in anticipation of the program, I experienced no feeling of pleasure.

When the speaker appeared, he was a tall, handsome, robust man with a vigorous, aggressive personality. His shock of heavy black hair was worn conspicuously long. His piercing black eyes darted swiftly this way and that as he gauged his audience before he began to speak.

Even with his unusual appearance, my interest was not aroused.

But when the first words came from his lips, an electric thrill went through me. The depth of tone, the roundness of enunciation, the clarity of diction, the sheer magic of speech gripped the whole assembly. The children, who had been fussing and fidgeting in their seats, sat still and enthralled, even long before the sense of the story could have had any message for them.

He told a simple tale which lasted for perhaps ten minutes. At the beginning, I was engrossed in his technic, but soon I fell under the spell of the narrative. Yet, when the speaker ceased, I realized that I had not taken in the end of the story—I had been wholly lost in the cadence of his voice.

Many times in the next few years I had the opportunity of listening to public addresses by the same speaker. Some were fairy tales told to little children, some were scientific discourses to learned societies, some were animal stories with the mimicry of voice and action in which he was so proficient; but it was after a long time and only by a direct effort of will that I finally became able to listen with my mind to the end of what he had to say. Each time I found myself at the close floating in a sea of resonance, a rhythmic ebb and flow of modulated sound.

It was not until years after—years of close association together—that we sat down, in cold blood as it were, and examined the elements that went into Ernest Thompson Seton's mastery of the art of story-telling. He had never approached the subject from an objective point of view, had never had theories as to his procedure. But, on examination, we found that we could dissect his unconscious approach, and perhaps, by the analysis, aid others to improve their methods.

And this is what we came to.

The art of story-telling combines the principles of short-story writing and of successful acting. It is, in truth, more difficult than either. The gift for it must be innate, but there is much that can be done to improve and cultivate it.

There is little doubt that the most important requisite for getting a story across is personal magnetism in the speaker. And it is important to realize that personal magnetism can reach only a certain distance, so that the closer, physically, the speaker can get to his audience, the easier will be his task.

It is always with a sinking heart that we take our places for a performance in an auditorium where there is a space of some twelve or fifteen feet between the platform and the group. It is as if there were a visible barrier separating us from our listeners, and there is a loss of rapport for which it is impossible to compensate.

The worst background of all is a gymnasium. The hard walls, which were never meant to enclose the kind of meeting where every modulation of voice has meaning and importance, throw back the words of the speaker and distract the attention of the audience in a horrible fashion. No sponsoring body has a right to ask a performer to present his program in such a setting.

It is always with words of apology that the chairman announces to us such a place of meeting, and there is little that can be done. But it is like asking a pianist to give a concert, and telling him at the start that the piano is out of tune and certain notes will not sound at all.

For a really appreciative group of listeners, it is necessary that they be not only close to the speaker, but close to each other. Elbow to elbow is best. Every gap seems to rob the spell of power, and there is no doubt that an audience crowded into a small room is far easier to win and hold than that same audience scattered over a big hall.

Also, it is far better if they be one body rather than several separate groups, part on the main floor and part in a gallery. For some reason, the gallery seems always to be a hostile crowd, ready to criticize, censure, condemn. They are a discordant element, and should be avoided if possible.

Another important consideration is the physical comfort of the audience. If they are seated on the floor, or on hard seats, or on seats without backs, the best storyteller in the world is at a disadvantage. The hearers must be unconscious of their bodies if they are to give full and undivided attention to the speaker.

Next, the audience must be protected from extraneous sounds and sights. A baby in the hall, a dog, the ringing of a bell, the passing of a train, or the sound of a late arrival can ruin the best story ever told. Even the loud song of a bird near at hand can distract the attention, until the elaborately woven thread is broken.

It is partly for this reason, as well as because it cramps dramatic style, that we always refuse to use a loud speaker during our lectures. The audience never loses sight of this intrusive element, and any amount of effort on the part of the artist is preferable to its use. In an academic address, there is not so much objection, and especially will the speaker with a poor voice do well to accept this aid. But for dramatic story-telling, the microphone is ruinous.

So much for the physical side of the problem—and, unfortunately, the speaker usually has little control over these essentials.

Atmosphere is the next element to be dealt with; often it is necessary for the story-teller to create the feeling he needs for his tale from the ground up. In order to do this successfully, he himself must visualize the pictures he would convey. Then, in every word he utters, in every gesture he makes, in every thought he harbors, he passes on to his hearers the setting for his story.

Sometimes mechanical means are justifiably employed to create and maintain atmosphere. These means may be carefully thought out and skilfully planted by the speaker, but they must not be apparent to the listeners. A very successful yet elusive, device is to conjure up certain feelings by the use of smell. The fragrance of pine needles, wood smoke, or salt sea can be enlisted to good purpose.

The next point to be considered is the suitability of the story to the time and place. Certain tales which may be perfectly proper in a men's club would be all wrong in a girls' camp. A ghost story is likely to fall flat if told in garish daylight. A noteworthy exception, however, is the story of "The Mackenzie River Ghost," contained in this volume.

A comic story, however good, may be absolutely unacceptable in a group of persons assembled for some serious purpose. It is always well to remember also that certain stories may be told with success in a very small private group, yet be wholly out of place and rightly censured if given to a large mixed audience. In other words, timeliness is a major consideration.

The length of a story is important also. Never tell a thirty-minute story when you are down on the program for ten minutes. Remember the anecdote about the man who ran over his assigned ten minutes, rambled on to twenty, and at the end of half an hour was still going strong. Suddenly, from the back of the hall, came an interruption. A voice called out: "Mr. Speaker, I see you are looking around for a clock. We have no clock here, but on the side wall you will find a calendar."

If some disturbance takes place during the recital of your tale, ignore it if possible. If this can not be done, treat it lightly or pleasantly. The audience will attach exactly the same importance to it that you do. If you take it as a joke, they will; if you get fussed, so will they. A fly walking across the lens when lantern slides are shown can be very distracting, or a slide put into the machine upside down can be construed as a great laughing matter. It happens to all of us sometimes, and the only thing to do about it is to make a passing lightsome remark, then—on with the show.

Always tell a story in terms of your audience. Occasionally this may mean changing the original diction, but there is no point in talking over the heads of your listeners and expecting dramatic reaction.

The story of "Gorm, the Giant of the Club," has been told many times by other writers. Several of these versions are full of literary value and charm of expression, but would have no lasting effect on a bunch of New York newsboys. As given in this volume, it grips the imagination of such a group by the vitality of the language and presentation. The same is true of "The Wolf and the Man."

Every professional story-teller who is likely to be called upon suddenly to tell a story keeps a list in some handy place, entering on the list each story in his repertoire—only by caption, of course. No one can think of exactly the right story at the right moment unless he has, somewhere on his person, a classified written group of story hints, easily available at any time. Do not trust your memory—or you will flounder at the crucial moment. Often a difficult situation, which might otherwise develop into unpleasantness, can be bridged by the right choice of a story. Happy the leader whose sense of fitness can meet such an awkward moment and turn possible tragedy into good-humored comedy in this simple fashion.

Throughout my childhood and girlhood I was naturally a good reader, and it took many years to persuade me that it was possible for me to *tell* stories without the printed page before me. But long, hard experience and an unusual teacher in my husband have convinced me that never can the reader, however good, make the indelible impression on the growing mind—yes, or on the grown one—that the story-teller can. And now I preach with the utmost sincerity: *Never, never read a story.* There is no magnetism, no contact of personalities, during reading. It is as if an actor on the stage of a drama carried a paper and read his part. The printed page between is an absolute non-conductor. You might as well be behind a screen as you speak: you will have just about as much power to move your audience.

The matter of applause is one to be carefully considered. An audience always has a better time if it can, in some measure, take part in the performance. In listening to dramatic stories, it is manifestly impossible for the audience to participate in active form. But it can do the next best thing, if it is permitted and encouraged to applaud.

Applause stimulates the audience as well as the speaker, and I have seen an unwise story-teller flatten the whole assembly and spoil his own performance by suppressing the first attempt at open approval.

Applause should be fostered and carefully managed. It is necessary to plan your story so that it gradually mounts to the supreme moment of action; then, when the listeners involuntarily explode into some demonstration, skillfully nurse the emotion back of it, and *pause* in your rendition until it has had time to spend itself. Then again, if possible, bring it about in a second round.

Of course, there are times when applause does not mean hand-clapping. Manifest approval is what we are aiming at, and the reaction may well be laughter, smiling, or nodding—may, indeed, even be dead silence. The last is the real tribute of deep emotion.

In planning your story, be sure that the climax comes in the last paragraph; if possible, in the last sentence; best of all, in the last word. It is ruinous to your effect if you provoke applause before you are ready. Anti-climax is deadly in story-telling.

Personalize, dramatize, your story, make it your own as far as possible by variants, by your own coloration, by impromptu intensification, by acting it. Tell it with your hands, your feet, your face, your whole person. Use gestures wherever they are helpful, but with reserve: only if every move means something. There are times when the best effect can be created by standing perfectly still.

All these essentials are the backbone of Seton's success as a story-teller. It is his unconscious use of all the fore-going, combined with his unusual personality, his abso-lute unself-consciousness, and his ability to relive a story hundreds of times, on every occasion when he tells the story, that forced John Burroughs, at the end of an attack on Seton's work, to finish his tirade with: "I must admit that Seton is the greatest raconteur in America" —an encomium which has been reiterated and enlarged upon by many critics, until he is acknowledged in the same vein all over the world.

Few of the stories in this volume are original in source with Seton, but he has made them so much a part of himself that they surely must be attributed to him and to his art as the best examples of successful story-telling extant.

JULIA M. SETON

CONTENTS

TRAIL AND CAMP-FIRE STORIES

LITTLE BURNT-ALL-OVER

✒

LONG AGO, BEFORE THE WHITE MAN CAME, THERE WAS
an Indian village at the south end of Lake Otsego,
and it it there dwelt a young brave with his wife and
little daughter, their only child. He was a good
hunter, she was a good woman, and their little girl,
then twelve years old, made their happiness complete.

The child was well educated, as her people understood education. She could make a fish-net; she could
set it in the lake and catch an abundance of fish; she
could split and dry the fish for winter use; she could
gum and paddle a canoe; she could follow the broken
twigs to where her father had killed a deer; she could
skin the deer, cut it up, and bring it home; she could
tan the hide into buckskin; she could make of this
war shirts and moccasins; she could embroider these
garments with porcupine quills dyed red with mis-
cawa and yellow with puccoon; she could make
vessels of birch bark; she could keep the lodge in
order; she could dance, she could sing, she knew the

"Little Burnt-All-Over" is a well-known legend among the
Eastern Indians. I do not pretend to any originality except in the
telling of it. It appears, in different interpretations, in the follow-
ing collections: Dorothy Tanner, *Legends from the Red Man's
Forest* (Chicago, A. Flanagan Company); Frances Jenkins Olcott,
The Red Indian Fairy Book (Boston, Houghton Mifflin Company,
1917); Gilbert L. Wilson, *Myths of the Red Children* (Boston,
Ginn and Company, 1907).

legends of her people; and last—but by no means least—she was a good cook.

The child was very happy in her home life, especially in the summer evenings when the mother would take her to sit on the western ridge to watch the wonder of the sunset. There, with His power and glory before them, the mother would tell of the Great Spirit, and of His unfailing care for all His children. The little girl listened with all the reverent intensity of her nature, gazing at the skies, while both her small hands rested in her mother's; silent, but sometimes asking some childish question to which the mother replied with a legend of the older folk.

As they sat one night, there was a sunset of such splendor that both were hushed and awed.

"Why is it so wonderful to-night, Mother?"

"It is a sign of great happening soon to come, my child."

Long they gazed in silence; then, as the brightness faded, there came on from the east a great veil of purple across the sky.

"What is that, Mother?" said the child as she looked.

"That, my child, is the purple robe of the Great Spirit."

Then, after a pause, the little one, both childlike and woman-like, said: "Mother, shall I ever have a purple robe?"

"Yes, my child, when your spirit is great, then indeed you shall have a purple robe."

As the color grew deeper and hid the light, the stars came out like points of white fire.

"What are those, Mother?" she asked.

"Those, my little one, are the wampum beads on the robe of the Great Spirit."

She gazed for a little while; then, harking back to her childlike thought, said: "Mother, shall I have wampum beads on my purple robe, when it comes?"

"Yes," said the mother gravely, "I think you will have many, many big bright beads of wampum on your robe."

As the child pondered these sayings, the mother continued: "Listen, dear one, the Voices have made it plain to me that I am to be taken away from you very soon. You are going to be left alone, and such sorrows and trials will be yours as never woman of our people has known. But remember this, you must meet them in a spirit of patience and fortitude, that they may pass away. If you meet them in anger and rebellion, they will come again and again, till the hard lesson is learned. Then indeed you shall overcome them, and you shall see them no more, except that each will become a bead of wampum upon your robe. And then such honor and joy shall be yours as woman of our tribe never before has known."

There were tears in the mother's eyes as she silently watched the last bars of splendor dying in the west. Both were silent for a long time, then they rose in the twilight, and went back to make ready the evening meal at the lodge.

Just a few days after this, the mother went out in her canoe to haul the nets; the north wind rose suddenly on that long, treacherous, ice-cold lake—and the mother never came back.

Now the little girl was left alone with her father. After the first sharpness of their grief was past, they settled down and were not uncomfortable, for the girl could do all things well. The lodge was clean, her father's clothes in good order, his war bonnet beautifully decked, and the food well cooked.

But he was a young man. He did not wish to live alone. He desired a wife.

Now it chanced that in the village was a young widow who had two daughters. She was comely, and so the young warrior went to her and said:

"I have no woman; you have no man. Will you be my woman? I will be your man."

And the widow said, "Yes."

So they were married, and she came with her two daughters to live in the lodge of the hunter with his own little girl.

Now these two stepsisters were well trained, as indeed were all Indian girls. They were not bad, but the older one was a little fat and lazy, the younger one a little thin and acid. They soon discovered that the little one was a better cook than either of them, so they let her do the cooking. She could make better moccasins than they could, so they got her to make their moccasins. Little by little, all the work was shifted to the hunter's child. And having begun to

give way to it, they became more lazy and then un-
kind. The father did not see what was going on in his
lodge; indeed, he was much away, and the stepmother
was careful, while he was home, to keep him from
seeing that his own child was little more than a
drudge.

One day the father went with a great war party
against the Hurons in Canada, and he never came
back.

Now, indeed, this family was in hard case, with
their hunter gone and none near of kin to help them.
One might have thought that the sorrows would bring
the family together in closer ties of real affection. But
it had the opposite effect: they became bitter with
each other, and especially with the little girl. For-
merly, they had done some of the work, the second
stepsister helping a little with the meals. But now
they became lazier as well as bitter. They even made
the little one bring their breakfasts to them in bed,
and if she was at all slow, or did not please them,
they thought little of beating her with a stick. Sometimes the handiest stick was one already burning in
the fire. Yet they would beat her with that, so that
she was covered with little burns on her face, head,
neck, and arms.

Oftentimes she could not keep from screaming in
pain, and the neighbors would come to ask what it
was about. Then the cruel stepmother would say:
"Oh, it's that little fool. She has no sense at all; she has
fallen into the fire again. Look at her. She is a dis-

grace with all her little scarburns. She is burnt—
burnt all over." And from this she got the only name
she ever heard now—Little Burnt-All-Over.

Sometimes the neighbors gave them a haunch of
venison, but nearly all that they ate now was fish
hard won by Little Burnt-All-Over from the lake,
corn from a tiny patch, and berries and roots that she
gathered in the woods. She knew nothing of kindness
or joy. Her life was one long slavery repaid with
cruel unkindness.

She had but one solace in it all. At sundown, she
would sometimes slip away from the lodge and sit on
the ridge, as she used to sit with her mother, and
watch the symbol of the Great Spirit go down in gold
and glory, and remember that in that was proof that
the brightness should come again. And when the
purple robe was laid across the sky and the wampum beads were shining, her mother's words came
back: "Such sorrow and toil shall be yours as woman
of our tribe has never known. But meet them with
patient fortitude, and they will pass away. You shall
see them only as beads of wampum on your robe,
when your trial is over, and such honor and glory
shall be yours as woman never before has known."

This thought strengthened her, and she went back
to her life of cruel drudgery without complaint.

And so four years went by. She was now sixteen, a
marriageable woman according to the custom of her
tribe. Her silent fortitude had filled her great eyes
with a lustrous splendor, and her mouth, always beau-

tiful, had now a gentleness and a strength that told of the tried and proven soul within. Her figure, always supple, was womanly and graceful now.

But the sisters had eaten up their own beauty with their evil thoughts and repinings, and their girlish forms were grown ugly with idleness. The stepmother was hideous.

Then there came into the village a rumor that set them all astir with eager curiosity. It was said, yes, openly told in council, that the King of the Snow Peaks was coming, the greatest chief in all the earth was coming in all his power. He was coming into their village to seek a wife.

Now every marriageable woman, maid or widow, wondered what she might do to win for herself this coveted position, the honor of being wife to the greatest chief on earth.

And many lay awake at night planning and hoping, and yet knowing nothing but the rumor.

But one morning when they arose, behold a wonderful sight. At the end of the lake, there was a new lodge that had not been there before. It was of great size and dazzling whiteness, and the symbols thereon told that this was surely the lodge of the King of the Snow Peaks.

Then the stepmother said to her elder daughter: "Now is your chance." She took her to the spring where they made their toilets. They put on her all the best clothing they had. With the help of the young stepsister, they hung on her dress all the elks' teeth and shell beads they could get. They greased her hair till it shone, and painted her cheeks each with a large spot of red; then on the parting of hair the mother painted a bright red streak. She looked at her, and said: "Oh, my child, you are beautiful; if he sees you, you will surely win his heart."

So, full of hope and pride, the big fat daughter went waddling round the lake to the shining white lodge. On the doorflap she scratched with her long finger nail, for one does not knock at a lodge. It was opened by an old, old woman with a very wrinkled face, but very kind eyes.

The girl said: "Mother, is this the lodge of the King of the Snow Peaks?"

"Yes, my child," was the answer. "This is my son's lodge."

"Is he in, Mother?"

"No, my child, but he is coming. I expect him any moment. He is coming into this village to seek a wife, and that woman shall be his wife who first shall see him as he really is."

"What way does he come, Mother?"

"Over those hills in the east, down that little trail," said the old woman.

"Mother, I am going to meet him."

"Go," said the mother.

Away went the girl, and as she began to climb the trail, she saw at the top against the sky a tall young hunter striding along. He had an eagle feather in his hair which waved in the wind. In one hand he carried the bow and arrows of a hunter, and in the other he held a thong by which he led two dogs.

The girl gazed till he was so close that it was rude to stare into his face; then she slipped aside and looked on the ground. As soon as he had passed, she turned quickly, but he had disappeared.

She ran swiftly to the lodge, and when the old woman opened the flap, she said: "Mother, I saw your son."

"Did you? And what did he look like?"

"Oh, Mother, a tall splendid young chief with an eagle feather in his hair that fluttered in the wind."

"What did he have in his hand, daughter?"

"The bow and arrows of a hunter."

"And in the other hand?"

"Why, Mother, he led two great hunting dogs."

"What did he lead them with?"

"I think it was a rawhide thong, Mother."

The old woman said in disdain, "No that was not my son, you didn't see my son." And she flapped back the lodge flap.

The girl went away weeping bitterly, for she knew that she had failed.

Her mother heard the story, and said: "Well, it may be that this great honor is reserved for your sister."

So the next morning they took the sister to the spring and put all the best clothes on her. They spangled her skirt with elks' teeth and shells; they painted her cheeks with two great red spots, and on her chin they drew three red lines as well as the line down her head between her plaits of hair. They hung a bunch of white shells on the end of each long braid; then they greased her hair till it shone. The mother looked on her with pride and said: "My child, you are wonderfully beautiful. If only he sees you, you are sure to win."

The thin girl went to the white lodge and scratched with her finger nail. When the old woman came, she said: "Mother, is this the lodge of the Great King of the Snow Peaks?"

"Yes, my child, this is my son's lodge."

"Is he in?"

"No, but he is coming soon. He comes down that trail on the eastern hills."

"Mother, I am going to meet him."

"Go."

So the thin girl began to climb up the trail on the eastern hills. Suddenly, at the top she saw a tall chief come walking. He had three eagle feathers in his hair, and he led two great hunting dogs as he strode in the full vigor of manhood. She gazed at him as he came toward her. She knew it was he. She took in all the details of his dress till he was so near that it was rude to look. Then she stepped aside and gazed at the ground. As soon as he had passed, she turned to see, but he had disappeared. However, the lodge seemed to glisten in the rays of the sun.

She ran down the hill, and when the old woman

came to the door, she said eagerly: "Mother, I saw your son. I saw the King of the Snow Peaks."

"Did you? And what did he look like?"

"Oh, Mother, a tall splendid war-chief with three eagle feathers in his hair, and they waved in the wind as he strode along."

"What had he in his hand?"

"The bow and arrows of a hunter, Mother."

"What in the other hand?"

"He was leading two great black hunting dogs, Mother."

"What did he lead them with?"

"I think, Mother, it was a twisted bark rope."

"What had he on his brow, daughter?"

"Mother, it was a wampum band. I noticed it carefully."

Then the old woman said gruffly and shortly: "No, it was not my son, you never saw my son at all." And she flapped the doorflap in her face.

The thin sister went home, bitterly weeping, to tell her mother that she also had failed. So the mother and her two daughters wept together.

Suddenly, they chanced to see little Burnt-All-Over, who was busy preparing the next meal. They did not want her to know or to see their humiliation, so the mother shrieked at her furiously: "Get out of this, you good-for-nothing," and she reached for a big stick.

The child dodged under the side of the lodge and escaped. There was only one place to go. She went up on the ridge where alone she was at peace; where she so often had talked with her mother in the happy days gone by.

As she sat there, the sun went down in all the glory of the Great Spirit. Never before had she seen so glorious a sunset. And when the purple robe was drawn across, it had never seemed so wonderful as now. The wampum beads came out brighter, more beautiful and nearer than ever she had seen them; it was as if she could reach them with her uplifted hands.

Thoughts of her mother came as blessing and strength, and her mother's last words of promise: "When you have overcome your sorrows, when your time of trial is past, such honor and joy shall be yours as never woman of our tribe has known." As she gazed, the purple robe seemed coming closer, and then into her heart came the thought: "Maybe that time is now."

She rose up in the morning before the others were astir and went down to the spring. She had no paint to put on her face, but she washed it clean. She had no elks' teeth for her robe, but the robe was neatly mended. She knew it would look better with shell dangles, but they had been taken from her.

She gathered some white flowers and made of them a border for her robe. She looked at herself in the spring and knew that she needed more, so she made a white garland and put it round her head. Again she looked and thought she needed something else, so she hung one flower on the end of each long braid of hair. Then she looked in the spring, and she knew that she was beautiful. Her beauty was not that of externals, but of a strong and valiant soul shining from her eyes, illumining her face.

She went down to the Great White Lodge and timidly scratched with her finger nail. The flap was opened by the old woman with the wrinkled face and the kind eyes.

Burnt-All-Over said: "Mother, is this the lodge of the King of the Snow Peaks?"

"Yes, my child, this is my son's lodge. I am his Mother Earth."

"Mother, is he in?"

"No, my little one, not yet, but I expect him very soon. He is coming into the village to seek a wife; and that woman shall be his wife who first shall see him as he really is."

"Mother, which way does he come?"

"Over those eastern hills, little one, down the trail you see."

"Mother," she almost whispered, "may I go and meet him?"

"Yes, my child; go, and bless you."

Away went Little Burnt-All-Over, and began to climb the trail. Almost at once there was a blaze of light against the sky at the top, and down there came striding the most wonderful being she had ever seen. She knew it was he; she had seen him in her dreams. Around his head were many eagle feathers shimmering against the sky, and she gazed at the weapons in his right hand and the wonder across his brow and the great hunting dogs that he led on his left.

She looked till he was so near that it was rude to stare, so she moved off into the bushes and covered her face with her hands and waited.

When she was sure he had passed, she turned slowly and with sinking heart to look after him. He was gone, but the white lodge shone with new splendor, and blue smoke was curling out at the top.

She went quickly to it. The old woman came. The girl began eagerly: "Mother, I saw your son. Oh, Mother, the tallest, most glorious war-chief I ever dreamed of. Around his head were what at first I thought were eagle feathers. But when I looked, I knew they were the beams of the morning light."

"What did he have in his right hand, daughter?"

"Mother, he carried the lightning. I saw it, red and crooked and forked and moving."

"And what in the other hand?"

"He was leading two great hunting dogs, Mother, white and strong. They were strange dogs, Mother. They had but one eye each, in the middle of their forehead. I have seen those dogs in the winter sky, Mother, in the lull when the white wind makes ready for a storm."

"And what had he on his brow, my child?"

"The rainbow, Mother—red, blue, and yellow, and shining in splendor."

"With what did he lead the dogs?"

"He led them, Mother, with a beam of light."

"Come into the lodge, my little one! You have surely seen my son."

She stepped aside. From the back of the lodge came the great Chief the girl had seen. In one hand, he held a purple robe spangled over with beads of shining wampum; the other hand he held out to her, as he said: "My own Little Burnt-All-Over, I have been waiting for you. I have been waiting till your years of trial and burning were over; till you had overcome your sorrows with patient fortitude. I have come now to claim you as my bride. Here is the purple robe you have won, for your spirit is great. On it are the wampum beads of your victories. Come now and dwell with me forever in the honor and glory that are truly yours. Men know me as the King of the Day. You they shall know as the Queen of the Night. And when they see your beautiful face in the sky, and your purple robe, they shall indeed see the scars of your sorrows and of your burning. But these shall in no wise mar your beauty, but be there forever to remind men that the way to perfect honor, glory, and joy is through the dark valley of sorrows overcome."

THE PEACE DAUGHTERS OF
KING CAPILANO

❦

THOSE OF US WHO HAVE BEEN PRIVILEGED TO ENTER Vancouver from the west will remember the two great peaks—twin peaks that rise high above the other mountains. They are draped in lasting white and stand side by side, looking out across the sun-down sea. The white men call them the "Lions of Vancouver," for they are in some sort like twin sphinxes.

But Teka Hionwake,* the Indian girl who told me this tale, had been misled by her white school-teacher when she so called them. She was sitting by her Squamish foster-mother as she said it. The old woman's eyes tightened up a little in protest, and her head shook vigorously in disapproval.

"Why, Mother?" said the girl. "Are they not 'The Lions?'"

"Nay, Hiona," said the old woman, using the pet name which meant that at least she was not displeased with the girl.

"Some day maybe I shall tell you," said the foster-mother. And Hiona knew better than to try to drag out the story, for any such attempt would have shut

---

* Pauline Johnson in white man's speech.

up the old woman like a clam that is rudely touched.

No, she wisely set the kettle on the fire and made some tea, then said, "Mother, will you have some tea?"

The old woman's eyes sparkled—she was pleased with the tea and with the attention. After she had drunk a cup, and the girl had lighted her pipe for her and shown eagerness to hear, the old Indian woman began:

It was this way, Little Hiona:

Long before the white man came, there arose a mighty war-chief to be King of our Squamish Tribe. Capilano they called him, a man of giant strength and of wisdom matched to his strength. He never sent out a war canoe but it was full of warriors. Every warrior was trained, and every quiver was full of arrows; each man had all the weapons that could help him to win. And ever they won. Village after village they took; tribe after tribe was overcome. When they found brave fighting men among the enemies, they adopted them into the Squamish nation; but when they found cowards, they slew them or brought them back as slaves.

And ever the power of King Capilano grew. His war canoes went up the coast ever farther, conquering and possessing, till they reached the Snowland that you call Alaska. And ever southward his armies forced their way, till they conquered and passed to the far Sunland that you call Mexico.

Then did he what never man had done before. Eastward he led his men on foot, and climbed the great Snow Peaks that none before had ever climbed. They reached the Buffalo Plains and met the Buffalo Indians. They routed them in battle after battle, for each of the King's men was a hero. Great bands of warriors were added to the King's army, and spoils without number: buffalo robes for all who wished them, and great treasures of weapons, wampum, beautiful vessels, lodges, canoes, and slaves. Many more Longhouses did the King build for the keeping of his treasures, and ever they were filled, and filled to overflowing.

Yea, all the earth now owned the sway of the mighty Capilano. All the world was his. Never before had so great a king been seen; never one so blessed by the gods of war and plenty. All good things were his; yea, every good thing, but one—the King had no child.

This was indeed a terrible grief to him, and ever he prayed to Sagalie-Tyee, the Great Spirit, that the cloud of sorrow might be rolled away. But the years went by; the kingdom grew mightier—and still Capilano had no child.

Then old Mowula the Shaman, the wise medicine-man, went up high into the Snow Peaks and built a fast-lodge. For three days and three nights he fasted and prayed that the way of wisdom might be made plain. On the fourth day, he stood again before Capilano, and said:

"Oh, King Capilano, I have fasted and prayed in the high mountains. On the third night the Voices came, and they made clear to me the way. This is their message: 'When Capilano gives to the Great Spirit his chiefest treasure, then shall he receive the thing he desires, and in the measure that is best for him to have.'"

Capilano's heart was filled with joy. At once he bethought him of his best treasures. Long ago, a strange war canoe had been wrecked on the coast. It was far bigger than the biggest war canoe of the Squamish. Indeed, it was built not of one trunk, but of many trees bound together. The warriors in it were of a strange race, and all were killed by the storm. Among the things washed up on the beach was a huge caldron of shining red metal. This was now in the treasure house of the King, his chief treasure, his most prized possession.

Capilano bade them bring the caldron. Then, with his war captains and wise men about him, he led the way up the river to the mountains where they are gashed two thousand feet deep by the mighty Fraser Canyon. Far down was the green and white flood; towering far above, the eternal Snow Peaks. And ever the voice of the Great Spirit rumbled there, proclaiming his presence.

Then, at the King's bidding, they lighted a little fire of cedar bark, and when it blazed brightly, the King took a pinch of tobacco from his pouch and dropped it on the flames. Soon there rose a long blue thread of incense smoke, ever the symbol of prayer, for it rises from the mystery of the fire below to the far mystery of the All-Above. And before it stood the King, and prayed as the Indian prays, with feet together, head erect, and hands reaching out as if to receive from his Father a blessing which he knows he will receive. And this was his prayer:

"Oh, Sagalie-Tyee, Great Spirit, hear me! Behold, I give to you the thing which is my best treasure. In all my kingdom I have no other thing I prize as much. Will you not in return give me the thing that above all things is my desire? Will you not now send to me a child, to carry on when I shall have passed to other worlds?"

He took the copper caldron in his own hands and hurled it over the brink. Far, far down it fell, to be swallowed up in the boiling flood.

Now the King's soul was lifted up. He knew that he had done well. He went back with a lighter heart to his war councils and his hunting.

So a year passed away. Then the great and wonderful thing for which he had prayed was surely coming to pass.

In his lodge sat the great King smoking, waiting eagerly for the coming of the old wise woman. She came at last and stood before him. He tried to seem unmoved, but his hand and his lips trembled as he removed the pipe, and said: "Well?"

"Good news, O King! The Great Spirit hath heard

your prayer and answered it." But there was a note
of reserve in the woman's voice.

"What is it? Speak out," commanded Capilano.

"Not a child, O King, but twins are born in answer
to your prayer." But still there was something in the
woman's voice which disturbed him—a doubt in her
face. The King caught it, and cried out in savage
terror: "What? Do they not live?"

"Yes, O King, alive and strong. But—but—both
are girls."

For a moment the King was dashed with disappointment. But he quickly recovered and said:
"Never mind, they are mine own children. They shall
be brought up as becomes their station. Each of them
shall marry a great war-chief, and two lines of warriors descended from Capilano shall rule the earth."

The girls were brought up with every good thing
that power could give: the best of training and the
wisdom that befits a woman and a princess royal were
abundantly theirs. They grew up beautiful young
women, beloved by all who knew them, worshipped
by their father, and altogether worthy of his love.

When they were sixteen years of age, accounted
marriageable women, the King, according to custom,
gave a great Potlatch, a feast that should be a worthy
celebration.

The King had grown ever greater and richer, and
at that Potlatch were gathered more great warriors

and wise councilors than it was believed could be found in all the world. A new Long-house was built for that day; there was none big enough in the village.

Bright new cedar mattings were spread on the ground, and food of every famous kind was in abundance. Sea and land, river and forest yielded their tribute. Vessels of wonderful make and of strange metals were there.

The guests were worthy of the feast, and waiting on them were hundreds of war-slaves brought from other lands.

At one end sat the Great King; and opposite, at the other end, the two beautiful blushing maidens. Proud beyond words was Capilano. This seemed indeed the crowning day of his life, with all the world to do him homage and his two lovely daughters entering womanhood, ready indeed for the crowning of his hopes.

And he was wise, too, in his hoping. He knew the instincts that were ready stirring to serve his purpose. He had not overlooked any move in the game.

Next to one beautiful daughter, Wihla, he had seated Young Kaga, only twenty-five years of age but already a famous war-chief, whose title was "The Fifty-Killer." He was tall and handsome to look upon, pleasing of speech, beloved of women. And the King, watching, mightily rejoiced when he saw the tender glances and whisperings that passed between Young Kaga and the maid.

By Wihuash, the other daughter, he had placed

Kalek, an older man than Kaga but still in his prime, the most famous of all the war-chiefs. His title was "The Hundred-Killer," and in power he stood next to the King. In Capilano's absence, he it was that ruled. And the crafty old King was pleased when he saw the great Kalek and the Princess whispering together and eating from the same bowl.

The medicine he had planned was working; now surely the last and greatest of his hopes was to be realized. And Capilano smiled for gladness.

When the feast was over, and the sacred pipe smoked round, the King spoke thus:

"My War-Chiefs, my councilors, my people, ye are here assembled for the great Potlatch, the coming-out feast of my two daughters. They are now to be accounted marriageable women; and on this, their potlatch Day, I promise them that they may ask whatsoever they will, and I will grant it to the uttermost."

Then stood up those two bright-eyed and comely daughters, and whispered together. And one, speaking for both, said: "Is it true, O Father, that we may ask whatsoever we will, and you will grant it?"

"Absolutely," said the father, "without let or hindrance. And I alone, on all the earth, could make such promise. There is nothing that I, the King, cannot grant, there is nothing that you may not ask this day. I, Capilano, have spoken."

He knew perfectly well what they were going to ask. Had he not planned and watched it? Had he not cleverly guided and led them into it? Without being told, he could see that one daughter was going to say: "Give me this day to Kaga for his wife." He knew the other would say: "Let me this day be affianced to Kalek." The happiness of the King was complete.

Then spoke one daughter for both: "This, then, O Father, is the request of your two daughters.

"That you set free these slaves who have waited on us to-day, and send them back to their own people. And send them back not empty-handed, but load them gifts, and give them safe conduct. And send by them a message of comfort to their people, to say that never more need they fear the warriors of Capilano. And send out also your swiftest scouts after the war canoes up the coast and down the coast, and after the war parties over the Snow Peaks, and bid them stop all fighting, yea, even though they be at the moment of a great victory. They shall stop the fight, set free the captives, return their spoils, bid the conquered foe have no more fear. And proclaim throughout all the earth that the end of war is decreed. Now shall there be only peace and good-will, for the Peace of Capilano is over all the world so long as the name and power of Capilano shall endure.

"This, O Father, is the wish of your two daughters."

The King sprang to his feet and staggered as though he had been clubbed. He seized his own hair plaits in his hands, and strained at them, as he glared away over the heads of his daughters and gritted his teeth. All about were dumb with amazement and fear.

In the silence at last the King spoke, and his words hissed out like separate arrows: "My daughters! My daughters! Ye have brought me very low. All my life have I been a fighting man. My chiefest joy has been to stand in the prow of my great war canoe and lead my band of heroes in the glory of the fight. My hope has been to have a son, a fighting man, who would take up the bow and spear when my hand became too weak and weary and carry on the name and fame of Capilano, King of all the earth.

"My hope and last wish was that when my time came, I should get out the old war canoe and man it with those that are left of my old fighting crew; and standing in the prow, I should shoot and fight— and fighting, die. This was my dream of a finish worthy of a great King.

"And now ye have reft me of that joy."

A pause, in which not a sound was heard in that hall of feasting. Then the King went slowly on: "Nevertheless, I have given my word. The word of a great King cannot be broken.

"Go forth, ye slaves, ye are free. Go see to all their wants, you my brave warriors. Send blessed medicine tokens with them, my wise men. Go forth, ye scouts, after every war party, a trusty scout to proclaim the end of war, the Peace of Capilano. Go!"

They stared at him in awe, but made no move.

"Go!" thundered the King. "Must Capilano speak twice?" And he reached for his war bow and a handful of arrows.

They sprang to their feet to obey. He glared around till the warriors all had gone. Only the councilors and the old Shaman Mowula remained.

With rolling eyes and moving but silent lips, the King glared around the empty hall, tottered, staggered, fell forward, and lay still on the matting.

There was a dead hush and a long, long pause. Then old Mowula went slowly forward. He raised up the King so all could see his face, and they knew that Great Capilano was dead.

Then in the Snow Peaks far beyond, there came the rumbling of a mighty thunder. And a cloud came rolling down between the peaks. It filled the valley and the canyon. It filled the village and the hall of feasting. The thunder grew louder and shaped itself into a voice. And all knew it for the voice of Sagalie-Tyee the Great Spirit.

Ever louder it sounded in the Feast Hall, and spoke:

"My daughters, ye have done that for which ye were sent. Come now back to me, and I will set ye on high, a monument for all time."

The voice ceased, and when the cloud had rolled away, the two beautiful daughters of the King were gone.

But that day, there appeared two new and glorious peaks in the sea chain of the mountains, higher than those around, twin peaks, looking alike, tall and stately as two women, draped from crown to waist with eternal snow, and looking forever across the sundown sea.

The white men call them the Lions of Vancouver; but we Indians know better. We know that they are the Peace Daughters of King Capilano.

KALOKA, OR THE STORY OF THE SEVEN SWANS

❧

LONG AGO, WE KNEW AN IROQUOIS MAIDEN OF THE royal line of Theyandenaga. Her Indian name was Teka Hionwake, but her foster-mother shortened it into the softer Hiona.

We knew her first among the colleges of Toronto and the East, for the folk of the chieftain's line were men of power, and the daughter was trained in the wisdom of the whites.

But the call of the blood was too strong. She withdrew from the big cities of the East and sought to live again the ancient way of her people among the mountains and islands of far Vancouver shore.

Still we kept in touch with her, chiefly by the written word. Of the many tales she told us, none had a better message or more vibrant truth than this, "The Legend of Kaloka."

Hiona's new home was in the village of the Squamish, on the banks of the Capilano River, with mountains beyond, and in between, glimpses of the restless ocean's blue.

Across the brawling Capilano was a bridge of logs. One day, as she crossed this, homeward bound, she heard the wild high call of the swans; and, looking up, she saw them pass above in marshaled flight—the leader, white and beautiful ahead, and, following in formation three to left and three to right—seven swans in all, a flying wedge, and they softly bugled as they faded in the blue.

The girl was touched by the beauty of their flight. As she entered the lodge, she told her foster-mother of the white array.

"What! You see seven?" said the old Indian woman, with interest aroused.

"Yes, Mother, seven snow-white swans."

"That very good. The Great Spirit must love you; he let you see Kaloka."

"What does that mean, Mother?"

"Little girl, you see that broken-down cabin at the high end of the village, and that ugly black rock that stand in front of it like a bad beast?"

"Yes, Mother."

"Well, I tell you. Long ago, we had in this village good hunter man, and he had a fine woman for wife. They very happy. They have two fine boys.

"But many times, when sun rise and make like fire on rock top, that woman go up that mountain side to that tall rock, the Spirit Rock, and light a little fire, and burn tobacco, and pray: 'Oh, Great Spirit, you so good to me. You give me a good man, and two fine boys. Won't you be more good, and send me one little baby girl? See, I burn tobacco.'

"But no little girl come. Long time, no little girl.

"Then, her man, he go to hunt on the Salt Chuck.

He paddle far to island. There on island, he see a big seal lie asleep. He make awful good hunt. He land on that island. All time seal sleep.

"He crawl up close. He make no noise, only carry club. He spring on seal sleeping, and with big crack, he kill seal.

"Then he look and see that that no seal, that sea otter, worth one hundred seals.

"He come back with skin. He shout: 'My woman, my woman! See, I make the best hunt of my life. Hudson Bay Company give me more than twenty ponies for that sea otter skin. I go now trade.'

"But that woman, she say: 'No, no, my man! Not Hudson Bay Company! You give that sea otter to Sagalie-Tyee, and maybe so He hear our prayer. Maybe He send one little baby girl.'

"That hunter man look long at sky and up mountain at Spirit Rock. Then say nothing, only nod head coupla times. Then he take ax and cut big bundle dry cedar and carry all up mountain to Spirit Rock. Right by Rock they make big fire. That woman she kneel by, and that hunter man he pray: 'Sagalie-Tyee, see, I come to give you the best hunt I make in all my life. Won't you give us just one little baby girl?'

"Then he throw that sea otter skin on the blaze, so all go up in smoke. A little tear come in woman's eye, but she know all is good.

"By and by when next spring flowers come in woods, there come some big happy thing. In that hunter lodge, there come one little baby girl, Oh, she so white, so beautiful. Her mother call her Kaloka, my little white swan. She all things good—only one bad thing: she have *one little crooked foot.*

"That mother she say: 'No care. I love my little baby girl. I make pretty mocassins to cover crooked foot. I love my baby girl.'

"Kaloka she grow up very beautiful. She can do all things good. She sew, she sing, she can cook, she can make good moccasins. She can do all things good—only one thing she no can do. She no can dance.

"In winter time, all the boys come to hear Kaloka sing. All very happy there, and many boys say: 'Kaloka, you marry me.'

"She laugh, and say: 'No, I stay with my mother. I no marry.' But every one love Kaloka.

"One day, a big black hunter man come from Thunder Mountain in north. He big strong man. He see Kaloka. He say: 'She cook good, she sing, she make good moccasins. She be good wife.'

"He say nothing, only go up high mountain, sneak up with bow and kill big buck. He drag it into village, push open Kaloka's door, throw down buck. Say nothing, only sit and smoke. He no look at Kaloka.

"Next week, he bring two deer, say nothing. By and by, a big bear. That big hunter man never look at Kaloka.

"By and by, Kaloka commence look at him. He so big and strong. She glad to see him come. Yes, now that big hunter see she watch for him come.

"He say: 'Kaloka, you take me for your man?'"

"And Kaloka, she say: 'Yes.'

"Then they have the big Potlatch in that lodge. Everybody happy, only maybe Kaloka's mother cry a little bit.

"That big man build cabin way up high end of village, and live with Kaloka.

"Years go by, and six fine boys come, all big and strong like him, no crooked foot.

"Then by and by, there come into village a girl from the Fish People on Columbia. She dance beautiful; everybody come see that Fish Girl dance. She no can sew, no make moccasins, no can cook, but she dance so beautiful every one come to see.

"That big hunter man look, and look too much. Now he begin to see Kaloka have a crooked foot, no can dance.

"Then that big hunter man begin think: 'I big strong man. I no want a cripple for wife.'

"So he say to that dance girl: 'You take me for your man. I go live with your people.'

"That Fish Girl, she say 'Yes.' So, that night, they go in canoe, down river to the big Salt Chuck, down coast south to the Fish People far away, then up the Columbia to the Fish Village. There the big black man build log cabin, fix it good.

"The Fish Girl, she laugh and dance, but she no cook very good. Big black hunter get awful tired, she never home when he come. One time, big man make long hard paddle on Salt Chuck. Get nothing, come back to cabin at night, all played out, starving.

"Fish Girl no there. He say: 'She dance awful good, but me no can eat dance. Guess I go back to Kaloka.'

"He gather much wood against cabin, light a fire. All cabin go up in smoke. He take canoe, go down Columbia into Salt Chuck, go north, paddle long and hard. Come to Fraser, go up and get to Capilano. There the village just like he left it. There the cabin he make when he marry Kaloka.

"He march up, open door. There on long seat on robes, sit Kaloka, beautiful still. And there, on one side sit three fine boys, and three on other side.

"That big black hunter man say: 'Kaloka, you take me back for your man?'

"Kaloka, she jump up, and stretch out arms.

" 'Sure I take you back. You are the father of my boys. Come back to me. Leave that Fish Girl and come back. I love you still.'

"Just as she say that, there come down the smoke hole a crack of thunder, and in the thunder a big voice:

" 'No! *No!* NO! She is too good for a black stone-heart like you! Go back to your Fish Girl! That is all you deserve. Go! *Go!* GO! She shall never more be your wife.'

"That black hunter stagger back to the door. He see Kaloka and the six boys rise in air and pass up out of the smoke hole. He see them rise, then change in form. He see only seven beautiful swans, three and three following the snow-white leader. And, as they pass to be lost in blue, they bugle in unison a far sweet quavering note that say: 'Farewell, farewell, forever fare thee well.'

"And the big black hunter show his true nature as he shiver and turn into a big black twisted rock.

"Yes, little Hiona, you see the ruined cabin up there, and the ugly twisted thing of stone? That is how they came.

"But Kaloka come often from the south with her boys, and bring a message over the sea. Yet not for every one alike.

"It surely must be that the Great Spirit love you, and give you a joyful message, when you see Kaloka and hear her bugle song."

THE STORY OF WOLVERINE

❧

ON THE FOURTH OF JULY, 1882, WE WERE CAMPED
with a lot of Indians and half-breeds near Fort Ellice,
at the junction of the Qu'Appelle and Assiniboine
rivers. Around the fire that night they were telling
stories of the trail and of the warpath. Some of these
stories were not of lasting value, but one there was
that thrilled me through and through. I shall not
forget it to my dying day—the story of "Wolverine"
as told by a gigantic half-breed named Tonka Jim
McKay.

He told of a small band of Sioux Indians who were
buffalo-hunting in North Dakota. Suddenly they
found themselves cut off from their own people on
the south by a much larger band of Red Lake Ojibway, their inveterate enemies. As this was a strong
war party, and the Sioux were encumbered with
women and children, there was little chance for a
successful resistance.

The Sioux fled northward, making for Fort Garry
(Winnipeg), knowing that the governor of the Hudson Bay Company would surely protect them.

At Fort Garry, the Sioux arrived and were kindly
received. An hour later came the Ojibway. The Sioux
were a little disgusted to see how small a band it was

that had chased them, for they never refused an equal fight. They agreed, when the governor insisted, that they smoke the peace-pipe together.

Three days later, the governor told the two bands that he could not keep them any longer. So Sioux and Ojibway set out toward the west. That night, they camped together.

Next day, at a place called High Bluff, the Ojibway held back, and when the Sioux rode down into a narrow defile, there was suddenly a murderous arrow and rifle fire from both banks. It was simply a treacherous ambush; and, in the fight which followed, the Sioux suffered heavy losses.

The half-breed told this story in great detail; then, finishing, he added: "Dat was Old Wolverine done dat. He was a bad ole Indian, but he was de biggest fighter dey had in de Ojibway nation. He was a big war-chief. But no good. He found his match at last."

As the half-breed said that, he made a gesture toward a big Blackfoot Indian, sitting quietly smoking at the other side of the fire—an elderly man, for I could see that his two long plaits of hair were streaked with white.

Now all waited for the Blackfoot to respond.

He blew off the four smokes, then stood up; and in mixed French, English and sign language, with dramatic gestures, told his story:

"Ha! Ha! Dat Wolverine big chief. Strong like bear, run like deer, fight like lynx, kill Sioux like smallpox. No good. Bigger chief come.

"Wolverine kill heap Sioux dat time by Portage la Prairie. He go, he find Dan Napao. Dan white man trader; he keep fire-water.

"Wolverine say: 'Dan, Wolverine big chief. Give Wolverine fire-water.' Dan give. Wolverine start in, get glad. Glad all night. Next sun-up, not so pleased now. Heap sick—here (head) and here (under belt). He say: "Wolverine heap sick. Go home.'

"He go, say to Dan: 'Me go, where pony?'

"Dan say: 'No got him.'

"Wolverine say: 'Dan, where Wolverine pony?'

"Dan say: 'My pony now.'

"Wolverine get big ax and say: 'Dan, where pony?"

"Dan say: 'My pony now.'

"Wolverine give Dan ax in neck. He go to corral—there pony. Wolverine ride off.

"Blackfoot on warpath now. Wolverine go with Cree for kill Blackfoot.

"Oh, dat Wolverine heap smart. He put on wolf skin, on head, on back, on legs, and run on four feet like wolf. Dat way, he kill buffalo, dat way he go scouting. He look like wolf—heap smart.

"Like dat way he come in bush right here, boy. Scout after Blackfoot. He no see. So he get up on hillside and den howl like wolf—Ow-ooooooooooo. Blackfoot in bush all time. He hear, he say: 'H'm, dat wolf.'

"Night time come. Wolverine get up on high hill. He think mebby he see Blackfoot fire. Blackfoot no fool, he no light camp-fire on warpath.

"Wolverine see nuddin. So he talk some more like wolf. Blackfoot hear. He say: 'Yeh, good sign, wolf howl.'

"Bimeby moon come up bright, bright like day. Wolverine on hill up high start sing moon song—Ow-ow-owowwwwwwwwwww. Blackfoot hear, he say: 'Dat not wolf. He talk too much.'

"He sneak on dark side hill. Wolf howl loud—he run. Long time come up on hill bchind. Wolf start more song. Blackfoot leap on him with knife, kill him dead, scalp him.

"Big chief Blackfoot, dat me; scalp on pipe now. Ha! Ha! Dat wolf he talk too much."

And the Blackfoot shook the scalp-lock at arm's length over his head.

HOW WAPOOS WON HIS RIFLE

In July, 1882, we were at Fort Ellice on the Upper Assiniboine, when a young Indian runner, Wapoos, arrived with very important despatches from Fort Qu'Appelle, 125 miles farther west. He had covered the distance on foot in twenty-five hours, without stopping. He was exhausted and fell as he arrived; but within an hour he had recovered and told the story of his packet with its life-and-death despatches. Also, he mentioned the promised reward, a Winchester rifle.

Next day, as I trotted alone the thirty miles that lay between us and the railroad at Moosomin, the story rhythmed through my mind; and at the end of my run, I set it down as here below, but took the liberty of making it a winter incident, to incorporate the hardships of another run well known to me.

The dogs had gone from Fort Qu'Appelle and bore the Garry mail,
And near a day had sped away upon the Ellice trail,
When tidings reached the lonely fort of warlike Sioux invaders
And swift destruction closing round the little post of traders.

Then grim old Mac, the captain, growled: "If only we'd
    'a' knowed
In time to send to Garry by them dogs upon the road,
We might 'a' had a fightin' chance to give them Sioux a
    rightin';
But now the only thing, my boys, is fight—and die
    a-fightin'.

"An' don't ye waste a shot, boys," as gruff low talk grew
    louder,
"We still hev quite a bit o' lead, but we're awful shy on
    powder.
I mean what I'm a-saying', boys, don't none o' ye be tuk;
Ye know the Sioux, but all the rest is doves to Thunder
    Duck.

"We haven't got a chance to skip, we're surely in a hole,
We cannot even ride for help, for every horse is stole.
They run the bunch last night, my boys, they surely
    worked their scheme."
The boys stood dumb, but every eye lit with a fighting
    gleam.

Then spoke a quiet Indian boy: "Wapoos go, paper
    carry,
Me run like deer, me laugh at Sioux, bring Redcoats
    back from Garry."
"Can *you* run?" said old Captain Mac, "where surely
    horse would fail,
Outstrip the dogs, outwit the Sioux, run forty leagues of
    trail;

"Save all our lives! Faith, if ye do, there's nothing ye can
　　ask,
I will not give when ye come back; small pay for such
　　a task."
The boy's eyes gleamed; his one great wish surged up,
　　his face flushed warm,
"Pas-kis-i-gan!" he pointed to a bright repeating arm.

Tall and slim was young Wapoos, but stout of heart
　　was he,
And tougher than ever a hill-born spruce, and straight
　　as a tamarac tree.
He bound in his belt some buffalo meat, the packet he
　　slung on his back,
With moose-hide moccasins lashed to his feet, he made
　　for the eastward track.

Behind in the valley his tribal lands, his lodge and his
　　people below,
Before him the plains, the fighting Sioux, and forty long
　　leagues of snow.
In the dim dull dawn he is eastward gone from the death-
　　doomed post out hieing;
In the light, bright day, o'er far Cotai, his fleet young
　　feet are flying.

Then the sun arose, and the wind arose, and the bright
　　snow blink was blinding,
But ever he glanced for a glimpse of his foes, and ever
　　the trail went winding.
Yet there were no sounds but the hiss of the sleet, and
　　the moose-birds' boding wail,

And the squeak of the moccasins grinding the snow, as
 he strode in the drifted trail,

And the rhythmic beat of his heart and his feet, and the
 sough of his steady breath,
As his strong legs fling in a moose-long swing; the land
 seemed a land of death.
No sign of life save the neat straight row of the fox
 tracks drifted stale,
And a coyote that followed with hope all aglow, and
 cantered behind on his trail.

With a tramp, tramp, tramp, and a tramp, tramp, tramp,
 nor ever a stop nor fail,
The sun was high and the blizzard nigh, and ever he flew
 on the trail.
Yet ninety miles to Ellice Fort, with blinding snow mis-
 guiding,
And the way is long, and the day is short, and the Sioux
 are riding, riding!

And he watched as he strode, for he knew that the road
 lay close by the hostile van,
He ran in the day and the dusk and the dark; he ran,
 and he ran, and he ran.
The coyote that cantered in hope on his trail, in hunger
 at last had left him.
With the moon o'erhead, still the brave lad sped, with
 his sense and his sight bereft him.

Trot-trot, trot-trot, like a wolverine! Fear, frost! Can
 naught confound him?

His food was gone, and his force undone, and the Sioux
    were all around him;
Then the clouds of night hid the waning light, and his
    strength and his heart were sinking,
With his pemmican gone, and the luck-bird flown, and
    the hackamore chains a-clinking.

Oh, the wild wind wailed o'er the prairie sloughs, where
    the Crees were crouched in hiding,
And the sky low grew and the snow flakes flew; and the
    Sioux, the Sioux were riding.
He halted him not in his long dog trot, away and away
    to the east,
And his only guide was the wind at his side, as he ran
    like a hunted beast.

With his moccasins worn and his mind fear-torn, still his
    limbs kept running unbidden,
By the gloom of the night he had held in affright, he safe
    from the Sioux was hidden.
Ten miles it is still to the Fort on the hill, when the gulch
    of the Cut-Knife he crossed;
With his eyesight half-dazed and his senses near crazed,
    he falls and he's lost; he is lost!

Oh, who shall e'er tell, when he stumbled and fell, why
    he crashed on a ptarmigans' bed?
From the deepest deep snow where the willow trees grow,
    with a thunder of wings they sped;
And the shock of their boom seemed to burst on his
    swoon, and he staggered afoot again,
And he rose to the track, with the gulch at his back, and
    he tottered away on the plain.

Then away and away in the dawn of the day, with a
 hope new and growing aglow,
Till he came to the height with the flag in his sight, on
 the goal of his quest below;
And he came to the port of the old Ellice Fort, as the
 dogs and their drivers outsped,
"Ka Kona! Ka Kona, the Sioux! Wah, the Sioux!" he
 shrieked—and is fallen as dead.

Old Garveny read of the tidings of dread, and he learned
 that this runner boy's run
Of forty long leagues in the fiercest fatigues was done
 from the sun to the sun;
And the news that he brought was sent on to the Fort,
 and the troopers and rangers came flying
O'er the wild western sloughs where the dread scattered
 Sioux went riding and hiding and dying.

Then rang all the land with the deeds of the band, those
 heroes who rode at the call,
But praises the loudest and honors the proudest, were
 paid to Wapoos over all;
So his gun it was won by his wonderful run, his kindred,
 his friends to deliver,
And his people still dwell by the Fort of Qu'Appelle, far
 away on the Who's Calling River.

THE HICKORY HORN-DEVIL

❧

RIGHT AFTER THE WORLD WAR, MY HUSBAND AND I were running a summer camp for girls in Connecticut. It was not exactly a charity, and yet we were doing it for love of the children, without a chance of monetary compensation.

Most of the girls were the children of well-placed Americans in a near-by town, but many were refugees from Russia and Poland, and I fear the Americans assumed themselves to be of a superior class.

Among the Russians was a little twelve-year-old girl named Ivol. She had been born a beautiful, a perfect child; but, as a result of the hardships of war, bad diet, or unknown malady, some fell disease had seized on and crumpled the poor suffering little body, till it was a shrunken caricature of a child. Her face was still beautiful, but racked by suffering. The eyes were bright, but the cheeks were wan and strained. Her legs were very long and spindly, and reached up nearly to her chin. Her neck was scarcely visible, and her golden hair rested on a hunchback that touched her ears.

Yes, she was a human wreck at twelve. But never once was there a word of complaint or rebellion from poor little Ivol. She was ever ready to wash the dishes or run errands for the camp. She hobbled slowly along, doing her best, and smiling a weak, wan smile at the joyous mirth of the crowd.

She could not go in swimming with the other girls, but she had a long, coarse bathing robe that reached the ground. She would put that on to hide her sadly twisted body, then stand on the dock and dabble her toes, and tell us what a good time she was having. It wrenched our hearts to see her brave suffering.

The American girls there were strong and beautiful in their youth. I fear they did not appreciate the silent martyrdom of the sufferer. We hoped to make them see and understand.

One of our regular rounds was to call at the tent of the leader, to discuss plans and problems of commissary. One dark rainy night, we called as usual.

After settling various matters with her, we sat back to relax. There were several of the older girls there. One of them said to my husband:

"Now, Chief, please tell us a story."

That was something he often did; and, since the group assembled were among the wild ones who often found it amusing to ridicule poor, helpless, tortured Ivol, he saw and seized his chance. He began:

"Have any of you ever heard of the Hickory Horn-Devil?"

"No!" they cried, somewhat startled by the name. "What is it?"

"Oh, he's the most awful looking beast in the woods. He's a worm only as long as your finger, but so horribly ugly and poisonous that every one hates him at sight. His body is like a crinkly toadstool, but covered with disease spots and slimy venom. Out of his back and sides are yellow and black horns that look like little serpents; and oozing out of the holes on his side is yellow spume like snake poison.

"Yes," the Chief added, as he noted the tense horror, "there is one right here in this woods.

"He is called 'Horn-Devil' because he is so frightfully ugly, and 'Hickory' because he lives high up in a hickory tree. He eats its leaves, and hides as much as he can under its dense foliage, and comes out chiefly by night.

"But he is not bad at heart, only a terrible sufferer on account of his ugliness—a lonely outcast without a friend, despised and rejected by all who meet him.

"One day there came riding by Mother Carey, the Great Mother Spirit of Nature. She heard him moaning, and stopped.

" 'Oh, Mother Carey,' he sobbed. 'Why should I be so ugly? What have I done to suffer this way?'

"Then Mother Carey, hovering near, said: 'Little Horn-Devil, you have an ugly body because once on a time you had a horribly ugly, poisonous spirit. Never forget, the body is the soul made visible. If you can discipline and reconstruct your soul, it will in the end create anew your body and give to it the beauty of a noble spirit. You must go through this life as you are, until the Great Sleep comes; after that, you will be exactly what you have made of yourself."

"Then the little ugly worm said: 'Oh, Mother Carey, I'll do anything, suffer all in silence if I can only win such a fight. Let me be twice as ugly if, in the end, I may be twice as beautiful.'

"Mother Carey looked at him long and sadly, then said gravely: 'Do you think you can stand it, little worm? We shall see.'

"From that time, the worm got bigger and uglier. No creature would even talk to him. The birds seemed to fear him, and the squirrels puffed out little horror-snorts when they saw him coming. Even the other worms kept away from him.

"One day he was sneaking through the woods, avoiding being seen, when in a sunny opening, he came on a chipmunk with her young ones, playing tag among the logs. They were so beautiful and joyful that he tried to come nearer for a better view. But the old chipmunk spied him, and cried: 'Run, children run! Here's a horrible, poisonous Horn-Devil coming.'

"They all ran into their den. The mother chipmunk came last and plugged up the doorway with clay, snorting with horror at the disgusting monster that had tried to come near her darlings.

"The poor little Horn-Devil moaned with sorrow. 'I didn't expect to play with them. I only wanted to see them, they were so beautiful, I am so lonely.'

"He hurried aimlessly away; but, as it chanced, he

went toward the barnyard. An old hen with her chicks was there. When she saw that bloated-looking beast come near her brood, she rushed at him in fury, dealt him a stunning blow on the head, then left him nearly dead while she led her little ones to safety in the hen-yard.

"Poor little Horn-Devil! For a time he lay stunned, but soon he made for the deep woods.

"As he dragged his poor body down the trail, a man came striding along. He saw this horrid reptile ahead and rushed forward to crush it with his foot.

"But suddenly there came from the sky above a thundering voice which said: 'No! No! Do not do that!'

"The man knew not whence the cry, but he stopped. That is, he did not crush the crawler flat, but scornfully kicked it aside, so that the poor Horn-Devil landed, bruised, wounded, and helpless, on a pile of leaves.

"Then came Mother Carey, and whispered: "How now, little Horn-Devil? Is your spirit strong or angry?'

"'Oh, Mother Carey, have mercy! I did not say anything; I suffered in silence. I want to win this fight, dear All-Mother!'

"'You are winning. By the strength of your silence you are winning. And when the long hard sorrow of your trial time is over, I will give you a body of such radiant beauty that all who see shall stand in adoration as you pass. Keep on, ugly one, you are winning your fight.'

"This helped a little, and he went on.

"One evening, as the sun was setting, he climbed to the top of his hickory tree, to eat his simple meal. Suddenly there alighted on the topmost twig the most beautiful creature he had ever dreamed of. A fairy, with gauzy wings that sparkled with silver and gold and robes of shining silk with precious stones for borderings! Never had he known there could be such an exquisite being. But, as he leaned forward for a better view, the fairy caught a glimpse of him, and exploded with a 'Faugh! Oh, horrors!' She spread her dazzling wings and flew high and away.

"A warning voice was heard: 'The Fairy Princess does not wish to be approached by a horrible, stinking Horn-Devil.'

"Oh, the cruelty of that blow! He was not even to gaze on beauty; and he fell to the ground, crushed in spirit as in body.

"Thenceforth, he hid by day; he come out only by night.

"And so the sad long summer passed. His only comfort was the gentle whisper of the All-Mother: 'You are winning. Keep on; you will surely win.'

"The autumn came, the time of shorter days and chill dank winds and falling leaves. There was frost on the ponds in the shade.

"The trees were bare when Mother Carey came.

"'Little horny one, your trial time has been long,

but it is nearly over. You have fought a brave fight. Prepare to sleep now; your reward is coming.'

"Then said Mother Earth: 'Because our little one has had unusual trials, he shall have unusual consideration. He need not even spin his hammock. Look, little Horn-Devil, see yonder sapling and the little hole beneath? Crawl down there, and rest.'

"Mother Earth received him, and he snuggled into her bosom. Mother Carey waved her wand, and he dropped off asleep, guarded and safely kept.

"For two hundred days he slept.

"Then came the Great Awakening, the Resurrection Day of the Woods. The heralds were in the sky, and all the world alive with coming life. New flowers appeared. Sleepers awoke from underground as Mother Carey's silent trumpeters went bugling ahead of her, and her winged horse, the Warm Wind, came sweeping across the meadows, with the white world greening as she rode.

"The Horn-Devil heard and upward crawled when Mother Carey called: 'Come out, little Horn-Devil! Come forth! Climb up!' He was still sleepy and cramped, bound up in silken strength. But new powers were his, and he was able to break the cords and crawl out of his hole.

"Then Mother Carey said: 'Where are your horns, little Horn-Devil?'" He fearfully felt of his head and his body—the horns were gone.

" 'Where are your plague spots?' They were gone,

and he found himself dressed in scarlet and gold, resplendent and bautiful.

" 'What are those things on your shoulders?'

"He shook himself, and realized that he had fluffed out wings, sweeping, glorious wings!

" 'Spread your wings, little Horn-Devil, and rise in the glory of flight.'

"He rose in the ecstatic joy of life and light just as the rosy sun was sinking, and went careering through the soft splendor of the coming night.

"As he flew, he glimpsed a radiant form ahead, a being like himself, with wings of velvet and gold. At first, he thought it was the Princess of the Hickory Tree; but soon he knew that this was a younger and more beautiful spangled princess, of a later and lovelier generation.

"He loved her with all his new-born soul; his heart was filled with the blazing fire of desire. Why not? Was she not of his own kind?

"Fearlessly now he flew to overtake her. She fled away over the tree-tops. But I do not think she flew as fast as she could, for soon he came up with her and was sailing by her side.

"At first she turned away a little, but she was not cross or frightened now. She was indeed inclined to play and tease.

"Then, in their own language, he asked her to marry him; and, in their own language, she said 'Yes.'

"Away they flew on their wedding flight, high in the trees in the purple night.

"In a garden below were some wise men. As they looked up, the youngest one exclaimed: 'Look! Look! Look! There they go on their wedding flight—the Royal Citheronia and his bride!'

"And as they flew, came Mother Carey, and whispered: 'How now, little Horn-Devil? Wasn't it worth the fight?'"

In that dank, gloomy tent of the children's summer camp, the Chief ended his tale. There was a moment of dead silence. Then the little girl who led the others in mischief took my hand in hers. My hand was wet with her tears as she said with a little sob:

"He has been telling us about Ivol."

THE BEAUTIFUL UGLY WORMS

THROUGHOUT THE MISSISSIPPI VALLEY, WE FIND THE beautiful Io Moth. Its wings are of brown velvet with spangles of gold, and in the middle of each wing is a great splendid eye like that on a peacock's tail feather.

Yes, the Io Moth is one of the most beautiful of all the kinds found in the woodland. But its caterpillars are wholly different, and in some respects, horribly repulsive. The chapter that explains this fact is a strange one in the history of the Io Moth. It shows that Mother Carey never gives any wonderful gift to her creatures without also giving with it some equal burden of sorrow.

This is how it all came about:

Long ago, when the new-hatched young ones of the Io Moth were small, they were, like most caterpillars, very ugly little things, so ugly that they felt very badly about it.

One day, they gathered together and set out for the great Home Place of Mother Carey in the Whispering Grove of the Ages.

There they prayed: "Dear Mother Carey, a boon! Grant us a boon! We are not of an ugly race. Why should we be so ugly as caterpillars? Will you not make us beautiful, for beauty is the best of all things."

Mother Carey smiled and waved a finger toward a little brownie, who came with a tray on which were two goblets—one full of bright sparkling rosy stuff and the other with something that looked like dark green oil. But the glasses were joined at the top; and there was but one place to drink from, and that reached both goblets.

Then Mother Carey said: "These are the goblets of life. One is balm, and will give you joy; the other is gall, and will give you suffering. You may drink little or much; but you must drink equally of both. Now, what would ye?"

The little ugly creatures whispered together. Then one, speaking for all, said: "Mother Carey, if we drink, will it give us beauty?"

"Surely, my children. The red goblet of life will give you beauty, for beauty is fullness of life. But with it, the other in equal measure will give you grief."

They conferred together again. Then the spokesman said: "Mother Carey, we drink."

So all the little crawlers went silently forward, and each took a long drink of the double goblet.

Instantly, they became the most beautiful of all caterpillars, brilliant jewel-green with stripes of pink velvet and gold. Never before were there seen such exquisite little creatures.

Away they went to rejoice in their new-found beauty.

But now a terrible thing happened. They were so beautiful that everything that fed on worms was eager to get them. Many beings that did not usually eat crawlers became their enemies and began to kill them, one after another. They were so brilliant that one could now see them afar—they could no longer conceal themselves among roots.

They crept off as fast as they could and tried to hide, but many of them were killed by birds and beasts of prey, as well as by big fierce insects.

They did not know what to do. So, next day, the few that were left came back to the Grove of Ages and once more stood before Mother Carey.

"Mother Carey, Mother Carey," they cried. "Have mercy on us. Another day like this, and not one of us will be left alive."

"Well, my beauty crawlers," she said, "what would ye?"

"Oh, Mother Carey, it is fearful! Every one seeks to destroy us. Most of us are killed, and many of us wounded. Will you not protect us?"

"You drank of the two goblets, my children. I warned you that your beauty would bring terrible trouble with it."

They bowed their little heads in silent sorrow, for they knew that this was true.

"Now," said the All-Mother, "do you wish to go back and be ugly again?"

They whispered together and said: "No, Mother Carey, it is better to be beautiful and die, for beauty is the best of all things."

Then Mother Carey looked on them very kindly,

and laughed aloud as she said: "Little beauty crawlers, ye have found the best of all things, which is a brave spirit. Therefore, ye shall not die. Neither shall ye lose your beauty. I will give you a defense that will keep off all your enemies but one—that is the long-stinger wasp, for you must in some way pay for your loveliness."

She waved her wand, and all over each of the beauty crawlers there came out bunches of sharp stickers like porcupine quills. They were worse than porcupine quills for each of the stickers was poisoned at the tip, so that no creature could touch the caterpillars without being stung. Man himself must let them alone or suffer a fierce rebuke.

The birds and beasts ignore them now, or receive terrible punishment from the poison spears. There is, as Mother Carey promised, only one creature that the beauty crawlers truly fear. The stinger wasp does indeed take toll of their race, for his great stinger can reach them long before their stickers touch him. But that is the price they still must pay for their beauty.

Did they not drink of the double goblet?

THE THREE SIOUX SCOUTS

※

ABOUT SEVENTY YEARS AGO, THE SIOUX INDIANS whose head village was at Minnewakan were roused to great excitement by the arrival of a friendly French trader who warned them that their inveterate enemies, the Ojibways of Minnesota, were preparing an immense war party to attack them. Since these Ojibways were known to have accumulated plenty of guns and a great store of ammunition, there was no reason to doubt their intention to descend on their ancient foes.

But details were lacking, so the Sioux decided to send their best scout, Whooping Crane, with two other tried and trusted men, into the Ojibway country to learn more of the enemy's plan.

In a good canoe, these three paddled rapidly down Red River till they came to Grand Forks, where Red Lake River joins on. Up this they went.

Now they were entering the enemy's country, so they traveled only by night, never using an ax, much less a gun, and even keeping their conversation down to whispers.

After four days of hiding and four nights of travel, they knew that they were not far from the Ojibway headquarters at Red Lake. Whooping Crane then mounted guard, while the other two carried the canoe far inland and hid it behind a huge pine tree.

They arranged to go scouting, each in a different direction, as far as possible into the enemy's country, returning the following night at midnight and signaling by a familiar woodland code. If they did not all reassemble on the first night, they were to try on the second. And if that also failed to reunite them, they were to try on the third. If all did not come together then, any that were left were to clear out, for it would mean that the enemy had secured a Sioux scalp.

Whooping Crane struck northward, protecting his eyes with one hand as he groped through the black forest, feeling his way with moccasined feet to avoid the breaking of a dead stick.

After a mile or so, he heard a faraway *thump-a-thump-a, thump thump thump, thump-a-thump-a thump thump thump.*

Ha! A council drum! Just what he was hoping for. He moved toward it as fast as he could, avoiding any unnecessary noise.

The drum call grew louder. Then Whooping Crane's sensitive toes told him that he had struck a forest pathway.

Along this he now strode quickly, and the drum grew ever more clear: *Thump-a thump-a, thump thump thump.*

After half an hour, he saw the tree-tops far ahead reddened by the light of a fire.

Ha ha ha! Now he was coming near to an Ojibway camp, just as he had hoped.

He came swiftly and silently toward it; and, here in an opening of the forest, he found a great encampment, a hundred lodges at least; and in the middle of it all, a war-lodge, a council lodge, from which came the steady summons of the drum: *Thump-a thump-a, thump thump thump.*

In the shadow of a huge tree, Whooping Crane approached and saw the assembling councilors. One by one they appeared and passed into the council lodge.

When the last one was in, the drum ceased, and Whooping Crane judged that now they were discussing war plans. He went quickly forward, and stood at the door, hoping to get a glimpse inside, and learn of their numbers, and maybe of their plans.

He was peering in so eagerly that he did not notice a belated councilor who came out of the gloomy woods and almost bumped into him.

Acting on a desperate impulse, knowing he was discovered, Whooping Crane drew his knife and stabbed the councilor to the heart. The victim fell without a sound.

Then Whooping Crane, realizing what he had done, exclaimed to himself: "Oh, what a fool I am! I've spoiled our whole game."

But suddenly another thought came: "Maybe not. Maybe this was just the clever thing to do."

He took the dead man's robe, wrapped it around

his own shoulders; then the war bonnet, and set it on his own head. Holding a fold of the robe across his face, he strode boldly forward into the lodge, and silently sat down in the vacant place. He did not speak to any one, but there was nothing strange in that.

He listened in on the council. He knew enough of their language and their signs to get the main facts: Yes, the Ojibways were preparing a mighty war party whereby they hoped to extirpate the Sioux nation. They had now plenty of guns and ammunition. They were going to assemble the whole of the Ojibway tribe in one army and strike with all their force at Minnewakan, destroy that, then go on to the next Sioux village with full force, wiping out one at a time. It was a very unusual plan for Indians to conceive, but it seemed certain of success if the Sioux were taken by surprise.

Having learned all he needed to know, Whooping Crane rose and silently left the council.

Soon after this, the meeting broke up. As they left the lodge, some of the warriors stumbled on the body of the dead man. A torch was brought.

"It's Two Elks! Dead!"

"No, impossible! Wasn't Two Elks in council with us?"

"But here he is, dead—and stiff too. Killed an hour ago!"

"How can that be?"

It was the high chief, crafty old Wolverine, who

solved the mystery. He remembered that Two Elks had not opened his mouth in council. This must be the work of an enemy spy.

"He killed Two Elks, and, clad in his robe, entered the council."

Now they know that, at any price, they must get this Sioux spy.

Whooping Crane traveled fast and far. He was a mile away when the pursuit began. He heard them coming through the dark forest, so gladly availed himself of the shelter of a hollow log. The rest of that night he lay there and all the next day.

He watched his enemies about and beyond him. It was fortunate for him that they were numerous, for their myriad tracks hid his trail from the best of trailers. Gradually, the sound showed that the pursuit had taken another direction.

All day, he lay in patient hiding; then, long after sundown, when the woods was black and safe, he set out to find his friends at the canoe.

Within half a mile of the place, he listened for calls; then, getting none, he began with the first of their arranged signals. He gave the long call of the hoot owl: *"Wah wah wa há wah wah wa há."*

After a brief wait, he got an answer: *"Wah wah wa há wah wah wa há."* Exactly the same as he had given it!

It might have been an owl responding; it certainly

was not one of his friends, for that was not the right answer.

So he silently glided off into the woods to wait.

After an hour, he ventured back into the neighborhood of the canoe; and, upon a slightly rising ground, halted and gave the call of the she-fox: "*Yap Yurrrrr.*"

In a little while, the response came back: "*Yap Yurrrr.*" Just the same! It was not the reply he had hoped for. It might be a she-fox answering back to a she-fox. But he doubted that very much. It was probably an enemy, and he judged it wisest to hasten away.

The rest of that night and all the next day he hid in a hollow log. Then, when midnight was near, he stole up toward the hidden canoe and listened long for a signal. Not hearing any, he gave one they had agreed on, the growling bark of the dog-fox: "*Grrrr-ow-ow.*"

Very soon, he heard a reply: "*Grrrr-ow-ow*"—the very same. A dog-fox answering to a dog-fox? No, no, very unlikely. In any case, it was not the answer arranged with his friends, so he withdrew as silently and quickly as he could.

At first, he was minded to give it up for that night; but, on toward dawn, he came and made one more attempt. He thought, as he listened, that he caught the faint, far moan of the timber wolf: "*Yow-ow-ow-ow.*"

So, presently groping his way to the shore of the

lake, he gave the rolling call that the loon gives at break of day: "*Hoo-hoo-hoo-hoo.*" In a few seconds, a voice replied with the same call.

Now he was sure that it was all done by the enemy. They were aware that he was in the country and were trying to decoy him. So he fled silently and afar off, nor rested until he was miles from the ambush.

All day he kept hidden and thought: "Alas, my two brave boys have surely met their fate. Now I must return alone to Dakota with the bad news."

Then he reconsidered: "No; that is not what we agreed on. We said we would try to meet for three nights before giving it up."

So, the next night, at the darkest hour, he came crawling, catlike, toward the appointed place—crawling like a man who is going into the very jaws of death, for he knew now for certain that the Ojibways were lying in wait for him and that probably both his friends were killed. Each time he raised his foot and set it down, he wriggled his toes, for fear of sound of dry twigs that might snap. Every branch that barred his way he crawled under or around. Not a sound he made. No lynx could have gone more softly.

He was still far from the canoe, and listening keenly, when he heard the soft howl of the timber wolf: "*Yow-ow-ow-ow.*"

A wolf, or a friend, or a foe? Which was it?

After due waiting, he gave the squawling call of the she-fox: "*Yap Yurrrrr.*"

Very soon, his heart leaped for joy to hear the

growling *"Grrrr-ow-ow"* of the dog-fox. It might, indeed, have been a real fox, but it was also the right answer. And, for the first time, a little comfort was his.

He softly withdrew and waited an hour before he came along the lake shore and called the common call of the hoot owl: *"Wah wah wa há wah wah wa há."*

The answer that came back was one that gladdened his heart—merely the long wail that the owl so often gives: *"Me-ow-ow-ow."* Maybe it was an owl, but it was the right response.

Twice now he had got the reply that they had arranged, and hope rose again in his heart. But his scalp and life were at stake, and he could take no heedless risks.

He crawled along to a safe distance and waited till the first streak of dawn was in the sky. Then, by the shores of the lake, he gave the loon call: *"Hoo-hoo-hoo-hooo."*

He waited, but heard no reply—which was better than the wrong one. Then he raised his hand to his mouth, and through the cupped palm, he howled the long soft call of the timber wolf: *"Yah-ow-ow-ow."*

It was no wolf whose cry came back, but a raven in a distant pine with his morning croak: *"Rrrrrrr."*

Whooping Crane laughed to himself with a little chuckle of joy. Three times the signal had been right, and hope was strong in his breast.

He waited, and soon his ears were greeted by the

soft sweet whistling of the white-throated sparrow. Another right signal!

He glided over to a huge pine near the hidden canoe, and with the handle of his ready knife, he tapped on the trunk the ordinary tap, tap, tap of the early woodpecker.

From behind the trunk, there stepped out a dark figure, and another. Then a familiar voice said: "How kola! Washtay, lillie washtay." (Hail, brother, all is well.)

And he stood once more with his friends and learned, even as he had suspected, that the night before, and the night before that, the Ojibways had been lying in wait for them, had discovered their trail, and had tried to decoy them into a trap. But, realizing the failure of the imitation calls, they had finally assumed that the scouts had fled safely out of the country, and so had abandoned the pursuit.

Thus Whooping Crane and his friends were able to get the information they sought, save their own lives, and warn their people in time, by knowing and using the voices of the woods at night.

THE DEATH OF THE OLD LION

❦

IT WAS A BIG BURLY NEGRO, A ZULU NAMED EM-VUBU from South Africa, who told us this tale. He had come to New York as a stoker on a tramp steamer. He spoke English fairly well and was gifted with that peculiar insight into the minds of animals that is often found in primitives and especially the black-skinned race of the Voodoo cult in Africa.

Originally he had been a farmhand on the ranch of a Boer in the open country beyond Orange River. His job each morning had been to round up the horses into the kraal.

Through a number of accidental circumstances, he had learned something about his master's activities that would certainly have put the man in wrong with the British authorities and probably landed him in jail. So the Boer made up his mind to get rid of the Zulu.

Em-vubu brought in the horse herd as usual one morning and announced to the Dutchman: "Horses is in kraal."

The Boer went to the kraal, looked the herd over, and said with severity: "Where is my little bay mare?"

"Dere ain't no more horses," replied the Zulu. "All is in de kraal."

"Don't you tell me that!" shouted the farmer. "I want that little bay mare I bought the other day."

"I don't know nothin' 'bout no bay mare," said the Zulu.

"You better learn something quick!" replied the Boer. And, taking down a big jambok whip, the Boer cracked it fiercely and shouted: "Looka, here, you black brute; get out and find that mare. If you come back without her, I'll cut you to pieces at the whipping post!" And he cracked the whip like pistol shots.

Now, Em-vubu knew that there was trouble ahead unless he could find a stray horse, so he prepared for a long journey. He put a lump of dry meat in his rucksack, hung a bottle of water at his side, sought out a good kaross or sleeping blanket, then, armed only with a knob-kerry or club, set out for his trek.

He did not believe in the story of the bay mare, but he tramped out far from the settlement into the wild karoo, looking for a horse or a track of a horse. But nothing was to be seen.

At night, he was many miles away and sought out a sheltering bank in a coulee, and there he made a fire and slept.

Next morning, he went on; and still farther on the third day. He was now on the far karoo, and ahead he discerned one of those African hills called a kopje. He made for this, sure that it would give him a good look-out, a survey of the desert around.

One side was a long slope, the other a perpendicular drop of 300 or 400 feet. Up the ascending side he tramped and easily reached the top. Here he had a wonderful view of the whole country.

He scanned it near and far, wondering if it was possibly true that the boss had a horse out here.

He saw no sign of a living thing until he looked backward over his own trail a mile or more. There he saw some dark object that seemed to move slowly, some wild animal, or maybe a horse.

He watched it intently. It came very slowly but at last was near enough to be distinguished. Without doubt, it was a huge lion. It was coming in his direction.

Now he watched with double interest and at length realized that the lion was *following his trail*. His concern now was at boiling point. He looked for some way of refuge or escape.

On the top of the hill were three ragged thorn bushes, not very high, but rough and strong. He selected the biggest of these and climbed up, hoping to be beyond reach if not wholly hidden.

The lion approached very slowly, and the Negro saw now that it was not on his trail, but merely following the same general line of travel.

As the lion reached the slope of the kopje, it went even more slowly, and now the Negro could see that it was a very old and sick lion, so old and sick that it could barely climb the hill. His tail was dragging on the ground, his ribs and backbone were sticking out, his head seemed too heavy for him to lift. He had to lie down and rest three or four times in the ascent. He trembled as he came.

He passed under the Negro without pausing or looking up, dragging his feeble frame a few inches at a time. He reached the edge of the cliff, and here he lay down for a long time.

Then, at length, he rose on his braced and tottering limbs, swung his great shaggy head this way and that, as he seemed to scan the plain, took a deep breath, and let out a long lion-moan—"*mmmmm.*"

The effort exhausted him, and he flopped down on his breast. But the end of his tail wagged a little, showing that he was pleased.

A rest of half an hour revived him. Once more he stood on his shaky legs, gazed to the right and left, and managed to utter a louder, stronger moan— "*MMMMMMMMMMM.*"

Again it was too much for his strength, and he lay on his belly for another long rest. But his tail vibrated more than before; he was feeling happier.

Another long wait, and the old warrior rose to his feet again. He looked over the world below him, took three or four deep hard breaths, "Hah hah hah hah," then put all his remaining force into a last attempt, and got out a vibrant "*R-O-A-R-R-R-R-R,*" a faint reminder of a lion's hunting roar.

When he found that he had done this, had at last voiced a real roar something like those he used to do, he leaped from that high precipice and was dashed to death and destruction, down, down, 400 feet below.

He knew that his days were over, his hunting ended, his strength gone. He could no longer live the life of a lion. If he kept on, he must live the life of a jackal, on carrion, offal, dung, insects, filth. On the other hand, he could come to this hill that he had known in the days of his strength, here view the great kingdom that once had been his, and in sight of it all, he could *die like a lion.*

That was what he had elected to do.

CLIMBING THE MOUNTAIN

It was Commencement Day at a famous school, on the staff of which were several teachers of unique ideas.

The distribution of the awards, prizes, and symbols of progress, was put in the hands of a prominent individual who strongly disapproved of all such things, so that each child who received a token of success received also a sneering remark. For example, the boy who won first prize for regular attendance was told: "Here is your so-called prize. If you valued it as little as I do, you would throw it in the ash-can."

A little girl who came out first with her embroidery was told: "Here is the prize which I consider trash, and the purpose of it folly. The fact that you have done the thing should be your sufficient reward."

He cast a cloud on the whole affair. He humiliated children whose parents had come to rejoice in their success and triumph. Many were in tears over his remarks.

I was on the program to close the exercises with an Indian story. But I did not wait for my time to speak. As soon as this teacher ceased his sneering, I arose. I was boiling with indignation, and said:

"I am down to tell you an Indian story at the

finish of this session. I shall not wait till the finish. I will tell my story right now, and you can tie it to the distribution of these prizes."

And there and then, I fabricated the following story out of elements which I had encountered before:

Afar in our dry Southwestern country is an Indian village, and in the offing is a high mountain towering up out of the desert. It was considered a great feat to climb this mountain, so that all the boys of the village were eager to attempt it.

One day, the Chief said: "Now, boys, you may all go to-day and try to climb the mountain. Start right after breakfast, and go each of you as far as you can. Then when you are tired, come back; but let each one bring me a twig from the place where he turned."

Away they went, full of hope, each feeling that he surely could reach the top.

Soon a fat, pudgy boy came slowly back, puffing and sweating. He stood before the Chief, and in his hand he held out a piece of cactus.

The Chief smiled and said: "My boy, you did not reach the foot of the mountain; you did not even get across the desert."

An hour later a second boy returned. He carried a twig of sagebrush.

"Well," said the Chief, "you reached the mountain's foot, but you did not even start the climb."

After another hour, a third boy came back. He held out a cottonwood spray.

"Good," said the Chief, "you got up as far as the springs."

A longer wait—and there came a boy with some buckthorn. The Chief smiled when he saw it, and spoke: "You were climbing. You were up to the first slide rock."

Later in the afternoon, one arrived with a cedar sprig, and the old man said: "Well done, my boy. You went half-way up."

An hour afterwards, one came with a branch of pine. To him the Chief said: "Good; you went to the third belt. You made three-quarters of the climb. Keep on trying. Next year you will undoubtedly reach the top."

The sun was low when the last returned. He was a tall, splendid boy of noble character; all knew he was marked for high emprise. He approached the Chief and held up his hand. It was empty. But his countenance was radiant as he spoke: "My father, there were no trees where I got to—I saw no twigs, no living thing upon the peak. But far and away I saw the shining sea."

Now the old man's face glowed, too, as he said aloud, and almost sang: "I knew it! I knew it when I looked upon your face. You have been to the top. It is written in your eyes and rings in your voice; it is vibrant in your frame. My boy, you need no twigs for token; you have felt the uplift, you have seen the glory of the mountain."

GORM, THE GIANT OF THE CLUB

🖋

IN THE YEAR 325 A.D., THERE WAS HELD A GREAT CON-
vention of the Church Fathers to settle once for all
a multitude of minute hair-splitting doctrines that
some thought fundamental and that others held to be
of little account; for example, "How many angels can
at one time dance on the point of a needle?" Or, "If
a portion of a man's soul is contained in each hair
of his head, what happens when a man cuts his hair,
or when he becomes bald?"

After some weeks of stormy debate, a monk from
the North Country rose up, and made his contribu-
tion in the form of a story.

This story Seton has given so many times to American audiences that the language has acquired an
American flavor, but the sense of the story is as it
was in the first telling.

———

In the North Country was a farmer of large hold-
ings. He tilled a wide acreage and had many flocks
and many dependents. He was a widower whose
family consisted of only himself and his son Gorm.

Gorm was a boy of remarkable stature and
strength. At ten years of age, he looked like twenty;

at twelve, he was over six feet high, and stronger than any man in the region.

He was tremendously proud of his strength, but his great joy was in his father. His father was the master of the whole farm. His father was the boss of all there was, and he rejoiced in the thought that he was the son of the "big boss," and next to him in authority. Nothing pleased him more than to have his father say: "Gorm, the men over there are idling. Go and stir them up; and if any of them is impudent, give him a crack on the jaw."

But it was seldom necessary to rough-handle the men, for they knew that Gorm was well able to beat any of them.

He kept on growing and developing, till, at sixteen, he was over seven feet tall, and built for strength.

One day he came on his father in distress over something. With ready sympathy, he asked: "What's the matter, Dad? Have some of the men been misbehaving? Don't you want me to hand some one a jaw-wallop?"

"Oh, son," replied the father, "I wish that was all it was. I'm afraid I am in wrong with the King."

"The King?" queried Gorm. "Who is he? You are not afraid of him?"

"Why, yes, I am. You see he owns the whole country and he could put me off this farm."

"Why, Dad, I thought you were the big boss, and afraid of no one."

"Alas, no!" said the father. "I am afraid of the King—every one is."

"Then, Dad, he is the big boss. I am the biggest, strongest man in all the country, and I won't work for any but the biggest boss. I am off to work for the King."

They could not stop him. Away he went, striding over the hills until he came to the Palace of the King.

At the gate, he was halted by the guard. "What do you want?" they asked.

"Is this the Palace of the King?"

"Yes."

"Then tell him I want to work for him."

They sent in word to the King. "Here's a big giant who says he wants to work for you."

"Show him in," said the King, "but guard him carefully."

So between two long rows of drawn pikes, the giant was ushered in.

"Are you the big boss of this country?" said the giant, as he towered over the King.

"I surely am."

"Then I want to work for you."

"Very well," said the King, and they made him one of the guards.

Here he had a fine time. He had little to do but eat and grow, and grow and eat; so that after three years, he was twelve feet tall and tremendously muscular.

Then one day, a runner came flying up to the

King's Palace shouting: "Pirates! Pirates are coming! They have anchored out in the bay, and are landing in small boats to sack the town."

"Send for Gorm!" ordered the King. As the giant strode into the King's presence the monarch cried: "Gorm, what shall we do? How many regiments do you want to meet this blood-thirsty horde?"

"Regiments? None at all!" said the giant. "Just let me at them with my club."

So, clad in armor that could defy their arrows, Gorm strode out to meet the pirates. The water, which was overhead for a common man, was only about mid-thigh for him.

He met the pirate boats, one by one. "Splash! Dash! Crash!" and down they went. Then, with his club, he cleaned up the pirates swarming in the water. Not one was left.

This done, he waded out to the ships riding at anchor, and jabbed them with his club deep under water, so that all went down, google, google down, and everyone of them was destroyed.

Now Gorm stalked back to shore in triumph.

All the country was crazy with joy. "Hurrah for Gorm! Good old Gorm with the club!" they cried. There was nothing too good for him. They were so wild in their cheers for Gorm that they quite forgot the King, and he was just a little bit peeved. "They might hand me some credit," said his Majesty, "and a couple of cheers once in a while."

But no. Gorm was their glorious hero and their protector.

One morning some months later, Gorm went to the King for orders. He found him pacing up and down, tearing his hair and raving.

"What's the matter, your Majesty?" asked Gorm. "Any more pirates coming?"

"Oh, Gorm, I wish that was all," said the King. "This is something you would not understand."

"Can't you make me understand?" said Gorm.

"Well, this is the trouble," explained the King. "I am hard up. I don't know which way to turn for money. Our treasury is empty, our army hasn't been paid for six months, and the men are getting into furious rebellion. I dare not add one cent to the taxes, and the whole bally kingdom is just going to the Devil, *the Devil*, THE DEVIL!" shouted the King.

"The who?" asked Gorm, bewildered.

"The Devil," replied the King.

"Who is he?" said the giant in surprise.

"Oh, Gorm, I hope you never meet him."

"Why, are you afraid of him?"

"Certainly I am, every one is," said the King.

"Well, then, he is your boss," growled the giant. "I thought you were the big boss, but you are not, the Devil is your boss. I am going to work for the Devil."

They could not stop him. He seized his club and went off in a rage, to seek for the biggest boss.

But he had no information; he knew not which

way to go. Nor could he ask any one; all the people
fled when they saw the great giant, realizing he was
in a bad temper.

So he strode away over the hills far into the country. As he went, there came slowly along the road a
small man, dressed in black, with a shovel-board hat
on his head, deeply engrossed in a book he was reading as he walked.

The giant stood still. The little man bumped
almost into him, and looked up in surprise to see the
great towering monster in front of him.

The little man smiled instead of running away, as
did most. This pleased the giant.

Looking down on him, Gorm said: "Friend, can
you tell me where I can find the Devil?"

"Yes, indeed," was the reply. "But you are going
the wrong way. The Devil doesn't live in the country,
he lives in town. Go right back to the city, up along
the docks to the red-light district. There at the far
end, you will find a house where they sell strong
drink. That's his headquarters, his office. If you look
in the door, you will see the Devil sitting at the table.
When you look in his eyes, you will know that you
have found him."

"Thank you," said the giant. Back he went to the
town, sought out the red lights and the drink house.
There, sitting at a table near the door, was a strange-
looking man, a skullcap on his head, with two little
horns peeping through. Around the leg of his chair
was something coiled that looked like a black snake.

"Are you the Devil?" asked the giant as he stooped low to peer in.

"That's what they call me," said the one at the table. He looked up at the giant; and when Gorm looked down into his face, he *knew* he had found the Devil. There could be no mistaking those awful eyes.

"Are you the feller that scares the King?"

"I scare everybody," was the answer.

"Then," said the giant, "you are the big boss, and I want to work for you."

"Good," said the Devil, "I guess I've a job for a fellow your size. Come on."

So they went out and smashed up the town. Then they went over the hills to another town and smashed that to ruins.

"Come on," said the Devil, "there's another town just over the ridge."

As they marched, they came to a curious low house by the roadside. It had a long, sloping roof; and at one end, a short square tower. On the top of the tower, there was a stick which stood erect, and across it at right angles another shorter stick.

"Look at this," said the giant. "Here's a new one. Watch me wipe that off the road with one sweep of my club."

"No! no! no!" gasped the Devil. "You must not touch that."

"Why not?" growled the giant. "Does that belong to the King?"

"No," said the Devil, now trembling with fear.

"That belongs to the King of all Kings. Come on, let's hurry away."

"Why, you are shivering. You are afraid," exclaimed the giant.

"Well, yes, I am; every one is afraid of the King of Kings."

"Then he is the big boss, not you. You are afraid like the rest of them, and I won't work for any but the biggest boss. Good-by!"

And the giant strode angrily away. He had been deceived again.

On he went, swinging his club in a rage. In blind fury, he swiftly tramped over hill after hill, following the high road. He could get no directions, for all fled at his approach.

But at last, going down a long slope toward a river, he met a little child.

The child looked up at Gorm, and smiled. The giant was appeased. He bent forward, and gently said: "Little one, can you tell me where I can find the King of Kings?"

"Oh, yes," said the child. "He crossed this river at the ford there, not long ago, and said He was coming back. If you wait here, you will surely find Him."

"Thank you," said the giant and sat down on the bank of the river to wait for the King to come.

All day the giant sat on the bank. Then, toward evening, an old woman with a market basket on her arm came down the other shore. She wanted to cross, but the flood looked so dangerous, she was afraid.

"Is there no one here to help an old woman across the ford?" she called.

The giant rose up from the grass where he lay and said: "Yes, Mother, I'll help you."

When the old woman saw the size of the monster, she was panic-stricken. But the giant said: "Never fear, Mother, I'll take you safely over."

He lifted her as one might lift a baby, and set her on the other shore.

"Thank you, good giant," she said. "I have no money to offer you; but, if a dozen eggs are any use, I'd gladly give them to you."

"Sure," said the giant, and the eggs were his ration for that day.

He slept on the bank until sunrise, when he was awakened by a shouting on the other shore. Here was a teamster driving a wagon, loaded with grain. He came lumbering down the bank and into the water, intending to ford the stream. But in the middle he struck a quicksand. His horses, wagon, and all began to sink. In vain swinging his whip, the teamster yelled: "Get up! get up!"

But they were helpless; all were soon sinking down.

The teamster in his terror shouted: "Is there no one here to help me? Oh, help! Help!"

The giant rose from the grass and said cheerfully: "Sure, I'll help you, brother."

The teamster, like the old woman, was scared by the size of the giant. But quickly Gorm came out, took horses, wagon, load and all, and easily pulled them onto the safe bank.

"Thank you, good giant. I have no money to offer you, but here's a bag of oatmeal I'll willingly give you."

"Glad to get it," said Gorm, and the oatmeal kept him for some days.

All day long the giant sat on the bank. Others came, and he helped them. Day after day, he sat there still, waiting for the King. More and more persons now passed that way, for it was soon noised abroad that a kindly giant was there, ready to help those who wished to cross.

All summer and autumn Gorm waited. Then came the cold weather. The giant had to build a little cabin to sleep in. He built it close to the ford, and never did he refuse when a traveler came knocking, saying: "Good giant, won't you help me across?" He demanded no pay, but took what they offered. Often he asked about the King of Kings. Some had never heard of Him, but some few said: "Yes, He crossed here once and is surely coming back."

So passed a year—and another year. Five years, ten years, twenty-five years, sixty years went by. And still the giant was at the ford, waiting, waiting for the King of Kings. Thousands he helped across, and still he was vainly waiting for the King to come.

Then came the most terrible winter ever known in that country. Intense frost prevailed for months, fierce blizzards of blinding snow, raging floods on the streams.

In the midst of the hardest time, in mid-February, when deadly ice and driving snow were menacing all life, there came during the darkest hour of the night, some one knocking at the giant's door. "Good giant, good giant, won't you help me to cross? I *must* get across."

The giant rose from his cold hard couch. He had never refused; the habit of a lifetime was on him. But he was no longer the big strong giant he had once been. Seventy years of toil and hardship had robbed him of his strength. His shoulders were bowed with labor, his back was bent, his knees were tottering. His immense stature, too, was reduced.

But he arose; and, leaning on his famous club, he tottered feebly to the door. He opened it, and here stood a *little child*. There was something familiar in the child's face and voice, as he said pleadingly: "Good giant, won't you take me across? I *must* get across."

With trembling, palsied hands, the giant reached down. In the days of his strength, the weight of a full grown man was a trifle to him, but now he could barely lift that little one to his shoulders. This finally done, he faced the blizzard storm, the blackness of the midnight, and groped his way to the ford. He staggered through the snow, almost crushed by his burden. When he reached the river bank, he found there a great flood on the stream, and shore ice had formed. The giant had to break the ice with his club before he could step into the flood; and when he had done so, the deadly chill of the ice cold water sent the very pangs of death up into his trembling rheumatic limbs and stabbed to his very heart.

But he staggered on. Never before had the water been above his knees. Now it rose as he entered the deeper channel till it was up to his throat. The little one had to stand on the giant's shoulders and clutch his hair to avoid being swept away.

Great blocks of ice came surging down and sent the giant almost off his feet. But he braced himself with his club and waited.

The poor old giant's strength was ebbing fast. He was nearly done for when he crossed the deeper channel. But the child encouraged him: "Keep on, good giant, we are nearly out. I can see the other shore."

They reached the edge of the shore ice, and again the giant had to break it with his club. He slowly dragged his old legs through, but the weight of the child seemed crushing. Finally, with the last of his strength, he was just able to seize hold on the willows and drag himself up on the shore.

As he did so, the child stepped from his once mighty shoulders on to the bank above, then turned and faced him.

The giant lifted up his sick and wearied eyes and saw—*WHAT?* A little child? No! A tall and wonderful man, with a crown of light about His head, and eyes that there could be no mistaking.

In a flash, the giant knew that at last he had found the King of Kings.

He flung himself at the Master's feet, and cried

aloud in agony: "My King and my God! Have I found Thee? Have I found Thee at last? All my life have I hungered to enter Thy service, and to give my life and my strength to Thee. But now, my life is gone and my strength is gone. I have nothing to give. I find Thee, alas, too late."

The giant was convulsed with the agony of his sorrow.

But the King laid hands on him in blessing and said: "Not so, not so, my beloved. On the day that you took your stand by this ford to wait for my coming, and to help those who had need of your great strength, you did enter my service. Whensoever you carried over the old, the sick, the helpless, the poor, the little ones, you carried me. Ten thousand times have you carried me over this dangerous flood. I have been watching you, I have been loving you, I have been preparing blessings for you. And I have come now to give you back your mighty strength and your glorious youth, that you one time did consecrate to me.

"And I will give you a new name. Men shall remember you no more as 'Gorm of the Club,' nor even as 'The Giant of the Ford,' but as 'Christofero,' Saint Christopher, the giant who carried the Christ Child. I will set your name on the heaven of heavens, a beacon for all time, as that of one who found the only true religion, which is this: *TO HELP THOSE WHO HAVE NEED OF HELP.* Come now, you shall dwell with me in peace and glory and honor forever in the Palace of the King."

THE HOLY GRAIL

❦

THERE ARE TWO WHOLLY DIFFERENT STORIES OF THE
Holy Grail. The first assures us that the Grail was
the cup in which Joseph of Arimathea caught the
blood of the Saviour when, on the Cross, his side was
pierced by the spear of the Roman soldier.

This story may be dismissed as a myth founded on
a pun. The blood of the Saviour was described by
the pious as the "Royal Blood," in low Latin "Sangre
Real," which the unlettered twisted to "Sant Grelle"
or "Holy Cup." And on this the legend grew.

The other, the true story of the Grail, is probably
as follows:

Every Jewish family of importance had a Passover
Cup which was a precious heirloom, handed down for
generations and used only at the Feast of the Passover, in memory of the delivery of the Jews from the
Angel of Death that was slaying the first-born of
Egypt. This cup was of pure hammered silver, undec-
orated. It held about two quarts of the Passover wine
and was handed around the table as a loving cup.

On the night before his arrest by the Roman
soldiers, Jesus, with his disciples, solemnized the
Feast of the Passover in the house of Mark, as related
by the Gospels, then went forth to meet his fate.

After the Crucifixion, a fierce persecution of the converts was begun. All who could get away from Jerusalem did so. Among these was the family of Mark. Hastily leaving, they took only their valuables and such property as was easily transported. There can be no doubt that the Passover Cup, their sacred treasure, was among the few things salvaged.

A group of disciples, including Mark, fled to Antioch, where first they were called Christians. They were for long in dire poverty, were hounded and persecuted, were daily in fear for their lives, but they held together, and strong in their faith, they faced the future without dismay.

The precious Cup was treasured, guarded, and concealed. It was the last holy relic of the Lord, the most sacred material thing in the world for them. They wished to render it secure for the future.

They were poor, often without food; but this devoted band saved their pennies, worked and scrimped, till, after some fifty years, they had enough money to employ a famous goldsmith to enshrine the Cup in an overcup of solid gold. This overcup was reinforcement for the silver which, as is well known, becomes brittle in time; and embedded in gold, it was safe from all ordinary destruction by wear or by disintegration.

In Athens, during the Age of Pericles, there had been a great sculptor who worked under Phidias and established a school of goldsmiths called the School of Scopas. It was famous for its embellishment of cups, vases, coffers, etc. This School passed out of existence about 70 A. D.

It must have been before this date that the Christians had employed the goldsmith who made the overcup for their Passover relic, for it is in the typical style of that School.

The Christians struggled and suffered, but slowly they grew in numbers, accumulated some property, and eventually built a small church. The high peak of prosperity, however, came with the Emperor Constantine about 306 A. D. Many treasures of gold and silver were presented to the church by the now prosperous converts.

But a change came with the accession of Julian, called the Apostate, to the Imperial Throne about 360 A. D.

In one of his marches, he halted at Antioch. The Cathedral was shown with pride, and there was much talk of the great treasures in the vault.

Julian sent for the Archbishop and said: "I hear you have great treasures in safe keeping."

The Archbishop bowed.

The Emperor added: "All those treasures belong to me, so bring them forth and turn them over."

The Archbishop replied firmly: "Those treasures belong to God Almighty, and I will never surrender them to a Pagan Emperor."

"Indeed!" sneered Julian. "I will return two weeks from now, and will then show you who is Emperor."

It so happened that Julian had to hurry back to Rome, but in due course his nephew arrived with a full legion of soldiers. Acting on instructions, he ordered the Archbishop and all his colleagues to appear before him with his soldiers standing ready.

"In the name of the Emperor," announced the general, "I command you to bring forth all the famous treasures in your vaults and deliver them to me as the representative of Caesar."

The Archbishop was fearless. "I will never surrender the holy things of God to a Pagan Emperor."

"Then fall upon him and his train," commanded the general; and in a few minutes, all were butchered.

The Romans then broke open all the vaults, and found them—empty.

The previous incident had given timely warning. The Archbishop had removed all treasures including the Sacred Cup. And not one man was left alive who had any knowledge of the secret places where all these precious things were hidden.

The greatest loss was, of course, the Holy Cup. To recover it became the search of the ages. More than one of the Crusades were organized with the main purpose of rediscovering the Blessed Cup, the Holy Grail; to find again the Passover Cup from which the Lord had drunk the holy wine. But all search had ended in failure.

In the year 1911, Cambridge University in England received a considerable legacy of money, with the condition attached that it be used for investigating such antiquities as had special interest to Christians of the established church; and particular mention was made of Antioch.

A body of competent archaeologists and Bible students was put in charge of an expedition.

At Antioch, they began excavating the ruins of the once famous Cathedral. They were much bothered by Bedouin Arabs who hung around, looking for alms or stray coppers. To utilize these, the scientists offered to buy any antique object they could dig up or find about.

The Bedouins thought it a great joke to bring in bits of brick, pottery, broken glass, copper nails, etc., and sell this rubbish to the Englishmen for real money, perhaps a penny or even a ha'penny.

But the Englishmen always paid promptly for these things, quite sure that soon or late they would find an ample reward.

One day an old Bedouin sheik was sitting by his fire, musing on the past and the present. After some silent thought, he said to his son:

"When I was a boy, I was one day going into the market at Antioch with my father. He had a purse with a handful of silver in it. He said: 'If I go among those thieves in Antioch, they will surely steal all my silver. It is better to hide it before we go near.'

"So we stopped at a grove of palm trees two miles this side of the city; and after nightfall, we buried our money exactly half-way between the two largest trees. Here we found it safe on our return trip.

"But, in digging down some three feet, we had come on an old pavement made of burnt brick. Maybe, if we go there now, we may dig up some of those bricks and sell every one of them to these fool Englishmen for good money."

Away they went with digging tools. The spot was easily located, half-way between the two largest palm trees. In a few minutes, they had dug down to the pavement. There it was, of very ancient kiln-dried bricks set in mortar.

After some hard work with pick and bar, they loosened and lifted a brick, and were amazed to find a hollow under it, evidently a vault of some kind. Other bricks were soon loosened and removed, and now they could see down inside. Yes, a vault about three feet high, and five or six feet square.

Close at hand was a pile of parchments. But, alas, as soon as the air got in, these turned to dust.

Near-by were five small silver cups, and standing much higher in the middle was a tall, sculptured chalice of shining gold.

The Bedouins were overjoyed at their luck. Now they had goods to exchange for real money, without doubt.

The boy was for going at once to the Englishmen with their prize. But the father was more crafty. He said: "No, we must work this just right to get the most out of it. I think we should first try Kouchakji, the banker at Aleppo. He is very rich and much interested in old relics. Then when we get his bid, we can go and play the Englishmen against him."

So they set out for Aleppo, with their cup carefully packed. The father said, and the son agreed: "If we get a thousand francs for that gold chalice, we shall be in luck, but we must ask much more."

Arrived at Kouchakji's house, the old man began: "We have made a wonderful find. It is something you will like. The Englishmen wanted to buy it, but we thought we would give you first chance."

He opened the wrappings, and carefully set the golden chalice on the table. The banker was profoundly impressed and heard the story of the find with great interest.

After minutely examining it, he said: "What do you want for it?"

The Bedouin replied, with calm and impudent assurance: "Fourteen thousand francs."

The banker looked at him with keen and penetrating eyes, then said: "Leave it with me overnight for study. In the morning, I will give you my answer."

Kouchakji had the reputation of being absolutely safe and reliable, so the cup was left with him.

As they went, the Bedouin said to his son: "I believe we will get a thousand or maybe two thousand francs out of it yet."

Kouchakji was a scholar and an antiquarian as well as a banker. He spent most of the night examining that cup, surmising its history. Clearly, it was an ordinary silver Passover Cup, worth perhaps twenty francs, but enshrined for some reason in a gold cup worth a thousand or more francs. Why? It was very ancient, maybe two thousand years old, if judged by the bluish tinge of the silver.

Next morning, when the Bedouins called for their answer, to their surprise, Kouchakji said: "I accept your offer. Here are the fourteen thousand francs."

The news of the great find spread quickly. The Sultan of Turkey heard of it and demanded the delivery to him at once of the treasure. Kouchakji responded by packing the cup safely in a bitumen barrel and sending it with other barrels to France, where it was hidden in the vaults of the Quai d'Orsay.

There it was when the Great War broke out. Kouchakji then sent it to America and deposited it in the Subtreasury Vault on Wall Street, New York.

When the World War was over, the banker brought it forth and invited Dr. Gustavus A. Eisen, the famous Orientalist, to come and see it.

After weeks of examination and study, Eisen announced that, in his opinion, this was absolutely and authentically the Great Chalice of Antioch, which is another name for the Holy Grail.

When this announcement was made public, all the rich men of New York came to bid for the cup. To each and all, Kouchakji made the same reply: "It is not for sale."

Finally the Pope sent a messenger to buy it at any price—millions if need be.

Again the banker replied: "It is not for sale."

"Then what are you going to do with it?"

Kouchakji responded: "That cup was hidden away by God Almighty at a time when it was likely to be desecrated or destroyed. He kept it hidden until now, when the world has reached its lowest ebb of materialism. He ordained it to be brought forth at this time, as a rebuke to the nations. That cup does not belong to me. God put it in my hands as His steward, and I will hold it till a committee of all believing Christians can get together and agree on a place and a shrine in which it can be protected and seen by all who reverently believe. To such a committee I will gladly and freely present the cup and resign the stewardship with which God has honored me."

On the 16th day of April, 1927, in my own apartment at Washington, D.C., some twenty of my friends had assembled, and with them was the tall and dignified Syrian banker, Fahim Kouchakji from Aleppo. He had been brought to tell us the story of the Holy Grail.

Here I have written it down from memory exactly as he told it that night.

I was standing near the door when he began, and I gazed unconsciously, in a hypnotic state of intense emotion, during the whole telling. I knew nothing of time or space or people about me. I know only I was gripped in a flood of emotion, in a whirlwind of fervent reverent intensity, as never before in my life. It was two hours before I came back to this world and took up again the train and thoughts of my daily life.

Before we parted that night, I said to Kouchakji: "Where is the Blessed Cup at this time?"

He replied: "In the vault of the bank at Fifth Avenue and 57th Street, New York."

"Would there be any chance of my seeing it?"

"Yes," he answered. "You and five friends might come, not more, because there is not room in the vault for more than seven."

He gave us the date—10:00 A.M., June 8, 1927. I, with five friends, among them Frank Crane, met him as appointed.

He took us down deep into the foundations of the bank, two stories below street level, and opened a large vault. In the middle of it was a green baize table; about this seven chairs. In one corner stood a large iron safe.

We were seated when the banker took out his keys, opened the safe, and brought forth a polished mahogany cabinet. He unlocked the door of the cabinet, and we saw something wrapped in a velvet robe. This he laid off; then in his two hands, held up the cup of shining gold, the Great Chalice of Antioch, with its simple inner cup of silver and its gorgeous protecting holder of sculptured and storied gold.

He set it on the table with these words: "This is the Great Chalice of Antioch. This is the Holy Grail.

This is the very cup out of which the Lord Jesus drank at the Last Supper."

We gazed with brimming eyes. After a long silence, I said: "May we touch it?"

"Yes, you may touch it, but not lift it. It is too fragile."

Each of us six, with bent heads, reached out and touched the base of the cup. The only sounds were deep sighs as all of us were plunged into an overwhelm of the deepest emotion. We realized that we were touching the most sacred and precious material object that exists on earth to-day.

THE MACKENZIE RIVER GHOST

ABOUT FIFTY YEARS AGO, SOME EMINENT SCIENTISTS headed by Sir Oliver Lodge founded a Society of Psychical Research to ascertain if there was such a thing as a ghost in the ordinary sense of the word. They offered to investigate every supposed ghost and to do it in the calm cold way of exact science.

Hundreds of instances were sent them; and at least 99 per cent of the ghosts were totally dissipated under the disintegrating white light of the scientific approach. But a few there were that would not dissipate, that defied all attempts to explain them away. Among them was the ghost of the Mackenzie River.

In his early days—that is the eighties—Seton lived in the Northwest and knew many employees of the Hudson Bay Company. Among them was one bluff old Scotchman, Roderick MacFarlane. After many years, MacFarlane was retired, and lived in Winnipeg on a small pension. Each time Seton was in that city—about once a year—Mac and he would have a pleasant reunion over a good dinner.

About 1904, shortly after the Research Society had recorded a ghost that defied all ordinary explanation, they were dining together.

"Mac," Seton asked, "did you ever hear anything about the Mackenzie River ghost?"

"What ghost?" said he.

"A ghost that came in broad daylight to some men on the ice of the Mackenzie River. The story was told by a Hudson Bay Company Factor."

"Humph," said Mac, "that factor was me. But Lodge and his group didn't tell it right, nor at full length. I'll give you the facts right now if you like. You can do as you please with it after I'm gone. Do you want to hear it?"

"I sure do," said Seton. "Go on. Tell it as long as you please."

And this is the tale as MacFarlane told it that night:

Away back in the sixties, the Company thought there was a good chance of a successful trading post at the mouth of the Mackenzie, since this was Eskimo as well as Indian country and there was no post within 400 miles in any direction. So, with Sandy MacDonald for helper, I was outfitted for the job. When the summer came, we went to the Mackenzie Delta; and then, turning west, we selected the mouth of Peel River, where we built a couple of log houses, gathered a great pile of driftwood, and were ready for any fur trade that came along.

Next spring, when the river opened, we had a visitor by canoe—a young fellow named Middleton, about twenty-two years of age, a graduate of Oxford. He came equipped with letters from the High Council of our Company. He was filled with missionary zeal, his one hope and dream being to preach the Gospel to the Eskimos. He had no knowledge of the Eskimos or of their language; but he was undaunted by these difficulties, for he felt he was the chosen vessel to bring them the tidings of salvation.

He was the most impractical, helpless creature I ever saw in the wilds. He knew nothing but his Oxford and his Bible. He seemed to us sometimes like a madman. But he came with letters from the boss, so we had to take him into our family.

Yes, we received him first only on the strength of the letters; but after a month or two, we were ready to accept him on account of his personal worth and charm. Far from strong, and troubled with a hacking cough, he was nevertheless always ready to do his share, and more than his share, of the work. He was the one who got up first in the morning to light the fire and start the breakfast. He was the one to wash the dishes or scrub the dirty floor. It might be a zero blizzard outdoors, but he was the one who volunteered first to go out after more firewood.

He had brought a fiddle with him. He played well and had a string of good songs, and many a long, dreary winter night he whiled away for us, with his music and fun. I tell you we learned to love that poor fellow like a little brother.

But there was something sad in it all—that cough. It grew worse, and in spite of his bright spirits and cheerful soul, he was plainly fading away. Toward the end of the winter, he was so thin and weak that he couldn't go out of the door without getting frostbit. His cough was terrible, and he was spitting blood. Still he was bright, cheerful, and hopeful, and worked steadily at his Eskimo Grammar.

Then came days when he couldn't leave his bunk. One night he called us to him and said to me: "Mac, you know I'm not long for this world; I've felt my Saviour calling me home. You fellows have been so good to me I want to ask one last favor."

"There isn't anything in our power you can't ask," I said for both.

"When my soul goes on," he says, "I don't want my poor body to be thrust into a hole in the ground like some animal. Won't you please bury me in consecrated ground?"

"If it costs my last dollar and my life, I give you my word as a man that I will carry out your wishes," was my answer, and Sandy and I took his poor thin hands in ours, and we gave our solemn promise.

I tell you we were blubbering like two babies. But he wasn't; he was bright and happy.

A month later, the end came. He passed away, happy and peaceful.

The nearest consecrated burying ground was at Fort Resolution, 400 miles up the Mackenzie River and fully 500 from our post. We had no right to leave our post now, so we wrapped the corpse in caribou hides. Then with our axes we chopped a grave three feet deep in the ice that never melts on the Mackenzie Mouth.

When he was laid in it, we filled it level with water; and within a few hours, it was one solid mass of ice, level with the rest.

We put a little marker at each end of the place, which was all we could do at that time. I tell you living with that kind brave soul had done more for me than any book or sermon ever did. And Sandy and I just prayed for a way to carry out our promise.

Well, sir, it was full two years we had to wait, and we surely felt bad about it. But the chance came. The High Council of our Company sent orders to close up the post and travel at once with all books and records to Fort Resolution, where we were to report to the Superintendent of the District.

This gave us the chance we had looked for. We had two sleds, each with a team of fine big Husky dogs. On one sled we loaded the books and records of the post, our camping outfit, and grub for ourselves and dogs. On the other, we loaded the corpse which we were able to dig out after a couple of hours chopping. Sandy drove one team; an Indian who had been working for us drove the other. I, the boss, trotted ahead to break the trail.

I tell you it was a funeral like nothing else before —a double funeral. First, it was the end of Peel Post. You see, we knew there was no chance of rival traders by land; but we hadn't reckoned on the whalers, who came by sea and wintered not far away. They did some whaling, but their best trade was in fur with the Eskimos.

So we left a lot of valuable stuff in the cabins and nailed them up to keep off the bears. We knew no Eskimo or Indian would steal anything—they never do—and when the summer came, the boat brigade would salvage all.

But our big thought was the other sled. We must keep faith with the dead man. And away we went in easy stages to cover five hundred miles of ice and snow.

The Mackenzie River is two miles wide at the mouth. It has gravel banks and runs through a wide plain with only level snow till the black line of the forest begins, three to ten miles away on each side.

The best traveling for the sleds is up the middle of the ice, for there the wind has blown the snow away, and the ice is clear and firm for the runners.

So each morning we set out up the middle of the river ice, trotting along for maybe twenty miles. Then we made our noon halt. Driving to the nearest gravel bank, we hauled up onto the level plain. But there is no wood short of the pine forest miles away across the deep soft snow; so, in order to avoid this hard trip, we always carried on the front of one sled enough firewood to melt snow and boil it for our tea, and then a little more to cook our bacon.

After an hour's rest, we set out again for twenty miles more.

Then at night, we would leave the river, and break our way to the forest, where we made a comfortable camp with plenty of wood. And I tell you, I always kept the funeral sled by my bed, for I felt under a solemn vow to protect that. In the morning we gathered a new bundle of wood for the noon and set out again on the ice.

This was our daily routine for about a week. Then one day at noon, after we had driven up on the gravel bank ten feet above the river, I found we had lost some of our firewood. There wasn't enough to melt a kettle of snow and then cook our meal. So I said to the Indian: "Take the ax and chop through the river ice. If we can get to the water, that will save half the wood we need."

The Indian chopped and chopped till he was down the length of the ax handle. But still he was not through the ice. He called, and Sandy went down to see if there was any show of the water.

Soon he shouted back: "No good." I said: "Then look for an air-hole," and went down to help the search.

All of a sudden, we heard loud cries from a human voice on the river bank ten feet above us.

"*Allez! Allez! Allez!*" it shouted. Then "*Marchez! Marchez!*"

We did not suppose there was a human being within hundreds of miles of us. But again came the ringing "*Allez! Allez! Allez!*"—the French that one always uses in ordering and driving the dogs harnessed before the sled.

In haste and amazement, we rushed up the bank and into view of our outfit. Here was the wide level expanse of snow bright in the winter sun, and *not a sign of a human being in sight except ourselves.* But there, lying in a groveling heap, were the ten big fierce Husky dogs, growling and rumbling, their eyes glowing, their hair bristling. The tracks showed plainly that taking advantage of our absence, the very first time they were left alone with the corpse, these hungry, half-tame wolves decided to attack and devour the body. But the moment they touched it, that ringing voice of command was heard driving them back in terror.

"Who spoke?" I asked almost in a whisper.

Sandy replied, also in a whisper: "Well, it was a white man's voice, for an Indian can't say '*Marche*'; he says '*Mush.*' "

"Who spoke?" I said to the Indian. He pointed with emphasis to the corpse and added in a low tone: "His voice."

I tell you we never took any chances after that— night and day some one of us always was next the body. We felt under a vow to keep it safe and carry out our promise.

Day after day and night after night we went on with the same routine, some days making forty miles, but on many days of blizzard storm making little or nothing.

Finally we arrived at the upper reaches of the Mackenzie, where timber was plentiful, and where islands with trees were right in the river; so we had no trouble finding good campsites.

One evening we came on an island covered with timber, right handy, and decided to camp there. Its shores were clay cut-banks about ten feet high. We left our two sleds on the ice, but Sandy and I climbed up. The Indian caught the dogs one by one, and we hauled them up onto the level top. Here we turned them loose, for I knew they would not leave the fire, and that ten foot drop was as good as a fence all around.

About nine o'clock, I was smoking my pipe before turning in, when I heard a strange faraway call on the wooded shore.

"*Ye-hoo-ooo-ooo!*"

I started up, for it was repeated.

"*Ye-hoo-ooo-ooo!*"

At first I thought it was a horned owl, or maybe a wolf call. But again it came with human intonation.

"*Ye-hoo-ooo-ooo!*"

"Say, Sandy, there's some one out there, a lost traveler." So I went to the edge of the island, and shouted back.

"Hallo! Hallo, there! Who are you?" There was no answer, even to a second call, so I came back to the fire. Very soon again there came:

"*Ye-hoo-ooo-ooo!*"

I went to the edge of the timber, and shouted: "Who are you? Why don't you come on? Can't you see the fire?"

There was no answer to this, and I said to my pal:

"Say, Sandy, I don't feel comfortable about leaving our charge on the ice. The dogs can't get near it; but anyway, let's put it up a tree."

So we three went down in the darkness; and after much trouble, got our burden safe up a thick bushy tree. We heard no more calls in the night.

Next morning, as my helper was packing and making ready for a start, I prowled around in the snow and on the ice. There I learned from the tracks that all the previous evening, and maybe for a couple of days before, we had been followed by a wolverine. Our charge would have been unprotected by the dogs and exposed to the wolverine, which certainly would have found and disfigured it, had we not acted on the weird warning that came in time.

After that, our journey continued with little incident till near Christmas, when we reached Fort Resolution.

There I turned over my charge to the Archbishop, who laid it by the altar in the church, promising to attend to all proper ceremonies as soon as feasible—which meant as soon as the springtime made it possible to dig a grave.

That night we three travelers slept in the rampasture, which is the name of the bunk-house in a Hudson Bay Fort.

The moon was full, shining on the snow, and, through the window, lighted up the place well. About ten o'clock I was awakened with a sudden feeling of alertness. I sat up as unsleepy as could be, and there right opposite to me were Sandy and the Indian both sitting up.

Then there came on me an overwhelming feeling of bliss, of happiness complete; and in the gloom, I thought I saw on Sandy's face the same expression of rapture. I do not know any word to describe the sensation but "ecstasy." It gradually faded away. We gazed at each other and at the door and at nowhere.

I said: "Sandy, did you see anything?"

"No," he whispered.

"Did you?" I asked the Indian.

He shook his head.

"Did you feel anything, Sandy?"

"I did," he said. "I was filled with joy."

"What was it?" I asked.

In a low but certain voice, he said: "He came in gratitude to us for carying out our promise. Thank God we didn't fail him! We have surely had our reward."

PINK AND LOUIE

❦

IT WAS THE FAMOUS BIRD MAN OF NEW ENGLAND*
who told us this tale, and I gladly repeat it as a
testimony to his intense and kindly sympathy with
the birds, and as an instance of his practical methods
in caring for them.

His garden, some two acres of ideal growth—lawn
and thicket—is in Cambridge, just outside Boston.

One fine morning in late April, he heard a new,
loud, ringing note that he had heard in the South,
but never before in New England. It came from the
top of a tall maple, and he rendered it to us as *Phew,
phew, phew, phew, woit, woit, woit.*

A swift and silent approach for a better view confirmed his instant thought. High-perched in the maple
was a glorious red cardinal, singing the loud song of
his kind, pouring it out with the fine vigor of his
race.

Springtime, love, loneliness, and red, red cardinal
blood were in its ringing notes.

Phew, phew, phew, woit, woit, woit, it sent out its
stirring message.

To whom?

The cardinal was unknown in New England. This

* William Brewster.

109

was undoubtedly an adventurous wanderer from the far South, seeking a new homeland but sadly disappointed at finding himself all alone in it.

Phew, phew, phew, he sang, and then the changing note was *woit woit woit*.

For an hour or more, the Bird Man listened and watched with intelligent sympathy. But not an answer came; not another of the kind was in ken.

Then came a bright thought. The Bird Man dashed to the local train, which soon landed him in Boston. There he sought out a dealer in cage birds.

"Have you such a thing as a female cardinal in your stock?"

"Just one," was the answer, and the dealer pointed to a little brown lady alone in a wooden cage.

"How much?" The Bird Man eagerly paid the price and hied him back to his Cambridge home.

There was the red, red, sad one high on his tree. The Bird Man quickly hung the new-bought cage with its captive on the side of his house near a window from which he could watch unseen.

Woit woit woit came from the red splendor in the tree-top. The little lady cocked up her head, and looked first out of one eye, then out of the other. Here was some one talking her language.

Phew phew phew phew-w-w-w-w it came again; and the little lonesome lady said softly *Pink*.

That was enough! Like a shooting star, that red minstrel swooped down from the maple-top, direct to the cage, as close to it as he could get.

The captive was alarmed by his energetic approach. She retreated to the farthest corner and crouched as though to hide.

But the red one cried out *Louie*, an endearing note in their speech. Still she hung back, interested though afraid.

Then the red lover flew to the lawn, picked out a big fat worm, and, returning to the cage, pushed the offering through the bars.

Still the fair one was fearful.

So he flew off to his song perch and sang anew with double force his love song: *Phew phew phew woit woit woit Louie.*

Slowly she responded; that is, crept forward and cautiously picked up the worm.

Not long after, he brought another.

Next day, the little play continued. But, on the third morning, the Bird Man saw Louie come to the very bars and receive from Pink's own bill the offered food. Now he was convinced that they had reached a complete understanding.

He went forth, opened wide the cage door, and retreated to his spy post.

After a moment's hesitation, Louie dashed out, and away, with Pink in wild pursuit.

For an hour or so, she seemed to avoid him. But his chase was ardent and persistent.

Next day, the Bird Man heard the ringing song from the maple-top, with softly interwoven sounds like *Louie*. And not far off, in another bush, was the little brown lady gliding about, seemingly not listening to the song. But neither did she go away, and once or twice the Bird Man heard her call her low *Pink*.

At last, he knew that all went well. He watched them with redoubled interest; and, after a week, he found in a thick lilac bush a beautifully finished nest with Louie in possession, and high on the maple tree her lover singing for joy.

Next day, there was in the nest a whitish-blue egg with brown specklings on it; and before the week was over, there were four eggs in the nest.

Now began the tedious work of hatching. The little brown lady went at it with devotion, while her splendid songster cheered her from the distant maple-top or brought her scraps of food.

For a week, all went well. Then, early one day, the Bird Man went for his usual inspection. He saw Pink racing about high and low, through the bushes and over the fence, screaming out *Louie Louie Louie*.

But there was not a sign of Louie, not an answer to his cries. The Bird Man hastened to the lilac bush which they had consecrated as their home.

Oh, horror! The nest was on the ground beneath the bush. Among the leaves lay the eggs all crushed and trampled. Here and there were little fine feathers, some of them bloody. Claw marks on the lilac bush trunk and tracks on the soft earth told the sad, sad story. The demon of small birds, the night-prowling cat, had found the nest, had slain the brooding mother, and desolated the lives of the pair.

All day, poor Pink went searching, crying in torment of sorrow and despair *Louie Louie Louie Louie.*

Not a sound there was to reassure him.

The Bird Man sat and wept. He knew.

Next day, the sad singer was heard in adjoining gardens: *Louie Louie Louie;* and each day farther, calling Louie, but no more chanting from the mapletop.

Savage vengeance on all cats was the only thought now in the Bird Man's heart.

He raised higher the wall around his garden, he finished the top with an overhanging net, he set traps for cats, he sat up with his shotgun.

A week went by. Pink had not wholly ceased his search, but now seemed saddened by despair. He did not dash about and call her name. He sat moodily, silently, in the maple tree.

One day the far-off call of robins seemed to catch his ear. He answered with a soft, low *Phew phew.*

The Bird Man was on watch. Something in that call there was that touched his heart; yes, offered him a thought.

He dashed off to Boston, to the dealer. He eagerly asked: "Have you another lady cardinal?"

"No," was the reply. "But I could get you one from New York."

"Telegraph at once, and have her sent on the fast express. I will meet it at the station."

That afternoon the Bird Man was on hand and received the cage with the little brown lady captive in it.

Away he went to his Cambridge garden and hung the cage on the very same hook as was used before.

Pink was sitting silently in a nearby bush. The captive saw his red plumes shining, saw the symbols of her own kind. She was very lonely and at length gave utterance to a low *Pink*.

He sprang to action, dashed about madly, glimpsed her in the cage, flew fast as lightning to the spot, saw her in behind the bars, was filled with joy—for a moment. But, as he pressed up close, he saw, he realized, it was not the right little lady. This was a stranger, not his Louie.

Crushed with disappointment, he flew slowly away and hid in the lilacs.

Next day, she called again, but he seemed not to hear. Still, he hung about.

After a week, the Bird Man saw him carrying a worm in his beak. The captive received it coyly.

Three days later, he was feeding her through the bars, and she eagerly receiving his offering.

This was complete evidence. So, next day, the Bird Man set the captive free.

Away they flew in the courting flight, and disappeared.

But, next morning, there came from the maple-top the loud *Phew phew phew phew woit woit woit woit Louie.*

The Bird Man mounted guard both day and night. Another nest was built, another bush was sanctified. Three eggs were laid, were duly hatched. Pink sang and foraged; Louie did her part.

And now there is a little colony of cardinals that dwell in Cambridge Town, loved and cared for by those who understand. They are descendants of Pink and Louie, who were the first settlers of their kind to build a home in that far north rugged clime.

THE STORY OF THE TWO POTS

❧

SOME TIME AGO WE WERE AT A SUMMER CAMP OF
well-to-do boys. It was suggested that they "do some
pottery." The idea was enthusiastically received. The
Camp Director sent for a good pottery teacher from
Boston. The pottery teacher got some pottery wheels
from New York, some beautifully prepared clay from
Trenton, New Jersey, some classical designs from
Italy, some fine pottery colors from London, some
beautiful sable brushes from Russia, a patent oil-
burning kiln from Chicago, worked with kerosene
from Oklahoma. And the dozen young enthusiasts
set to work.

They were quick to learn. Each one selected a
design and made a careful copy of it in the prepared
clay. This was set away to dry. After it was finished,
it was partly fired; then each little potter painted
with his exquisite brush a copy of a beautiful classical decoration. These were touched up by the teacher
and dried. The kiln was then heated up, and each pot
was perfectly fired and finally glazed. So each little
potter got a really beautiful vase to take home to his
proud parents, at a cost to them of twenty-five dol-
lars per vase.

At another camp not far away, we were again

visiting. The boys wanted to "do some pottery," and they consulted us. Seton said: "Do you wish to do it in the regular school method, or in the real Woodcraft way?" They said they preferred the Woodcraft way.

"Good," said the Chief. "Now who knows where there is any clay?"

"I know. There is a streak of yellow in the railway cutting," said one boy.

"And I found a lot in the bottom of the creek when I fell in the other day," said another. "I came out all blue."

"Fine. Now we want two expeditions—one to the railroad cutting, and one to the creek; and get each a lump of clay as big as a cocoanut."

When they had returned with their loads, we went to the edge of the pond. There we picked out all the pebbles and straws and worked up the clay with a little water till it was soft and even in grain throughout.

Now we halted for dinner, after which Seton said: "Each boy needs a flat board about a foot square, a knife, and something to hold about a pint of water."

The gang soon appeared with a variety of knives, and water in old tomato tins.

We showed them how to roll the clay out flat on the board and cut it into "shoe laces" about half an inch thick; then coil these into a little saucer shape, soldering the coils together by rubbing them with wet finger tips.

When the saucers were about three inches wide, we set them away to dry for an hour or more.

Then, after wetting the edge, we added coils of clay vertically, till the saucers became low cups, about four inches wide and two inches high. Again they were set aside to harden. Finally, a finish was given by drawing in the top of the cup a little. While these were drying in the shade, we set about getting colors.

"Who knows where we can get some lime?" Seton asked.

"I do," shouted one enterprising youngster. "Just down by the cowbarn where they built a concrete drinking trough. There must be a quart at least lying about on the ground."

"Good!" was the reply. "I appoint you a committee of one to bring us a canful of lime. Now, who knows where there is some red brick?"

"Oh, I know," spoke up a little fellow. "Right down where they laid a new walk back of the main house. There ain't no whole bricks, but lots of broken pieces."

"Fine!" Seton applauded. "Now you go down there, and bring back two handfuls of broken red brick."

Off he sped.

"Now, who knows where I can get some black soot?"

They seemed stumped. No one knew where to find this.

"Then I'll tell you," Seton said. "Go to the camp

kitchen and ask the cook to let you scrape the under-
side of the stove lids. That is the best kind of black
—indeed, as children we always used that to black
our boots on Sunday."

A volunteer offered to carry out this suggestion
and was off.

Meanwhile, we procured some flat stones, and when
all were reassembled, we handed out a stone to each
boy. On these, we ground up our lime, brick and soot,
in separate piles.

Upon inquiry, we learned that down by the brook
was a pile of clamshells left after a feast by the
'coons. Some of these were brought quickly and dis-
tributed.

Now, in one shell, we mixed some powdered lime
with clay and water so that it was like white cream.

In another, powdered brick was mixed with clay
and water for red; and soot and clay with water in
the last gave us our black.

"Now for the brushes. Who knows where there was
a hickory tree cut down last winter?"

We soon located such a place; and found in the
middle of the stump the usual row of stiff slivers left
on the tree broken near the ground. These are sea-
soned heart wood.

Each boy cut and rounded a sliver, then chewed
the end into a soft brush. Now we were ready.

The pots were scraped and rubbed over with slip
or clay cream, till they were in good finish. After
they had dried once more, we began to paint them

with our prepared colors. The designs were not very classical, but they had some relation to our camp life. Several boys used their names and camp emblems; some drew animals. No two decorations were alike. None of them were very high as art.

These final products were set away over the stove for complete drying—and this means bone-dry without a trace of moisture. At least two days are needed for this.

Now we prepared for the firing. We laid the pots on the ground in rows, with small logs between them, then carefully built up a three-foot pyramid of good firewood and set it going.

The pile blazed like a furnace. After an hour it began to shrink a little, and I caught a glimpse of one of the pots. It was of a beautiful glowing cherry red. In our hurry to see the result, I got a long pole and fished out the pot. Alas! As soon as it was touched by the cool air, it opened out into twenty pieces. This taught us a lesson—the lesson of patience. We left the rest under the glowing pile all day.

The next morning, the fire was dead; and under the ashes, we found our pots, now cool and finished—one or two broken, one or two with hairlike cracks, but half a dozen of sound, hard, ringing terra-cotta with the designs burnt in red, black and white on the yellow ground of the clay. They were serviceable, passable pots, not only a joy, but a glory to each of the proud owners.

Now, frankly, would our Woodcraft pots compare

in any way with those produced by the class with the imported and bought materials? No, not for a moment. Theirs were very good; ours very, very poor. But the school potters had learned little and had forgotten it all in a year. Our boys learned much and will never forget it. As long as they live, they will have a new and self-reliant attitude toward certain forces and materials in nature. In a word, the first class was for making pots; the second class was for making boys.

We each got what we went after.

CROK AND THE CROCODILE

THE FIRST WORD HE SAID WAS "MAM MAM," THE
second was "Goo goo"—which was quite the usual
thing. But the third was "Crok crok." This was quite
unusual, and it came months later. It was prompted
by hearing a raven make similar sounds as it flew
over—and that was why they named him "Crok."

This incident showed that Crok was an observer,
as well as gifted with good control of his muscles.
These things grew with him; so that, at the age of
fifteen, Crok was a big, strong young hunter, well
able to take care of himself in all the ordinary stress
of life in the woods.

With the backward ken of history, I saw him
standing on a ledge by the water—naked, brown,
sinewy, strong, alert. This way and that he peered:
every log in sight or partly hidden by the bushes, the
water, or the bend of the bank, was keenly viewed
and quickly comprehended. Not a line of bubbles in
the stream but was seen and understood, for Crok
had come to the ford, the crossing of the river, and
he must pass. Although but fifteen years old, his
father had sent him with word to another camp, and
it was his job to get there as best he might.

The woods were full of dangers; so was the open.

But the dread of all was the crocodiles in the river. Experience had taught the crocodiles that this was a favorite place for many kinds of prey to cross, and it was their custom to lie in wait for the chances offered.

Keeping out of sight himself, Crok looked well about. Then, grasping his stone club by the handle, with the thong slipped over his wrist, he dropped low, strode fast through the shallow water, came to the full, deep channel, plunged quietly, struck out with strong, sweeping strokes, and reached a rocky island in the middle. Quickly climbing up on this, he searched with his eye the current behind, before, and around him. No ripple was there to signal an enemy.

So, taking a good breath, he dived off the rock into the farther flood, swam under for a distance, came up, flung his dripping hair from his eyes, and silently struck out for the farther shore, where he landed in good time and glided out into the woods. There, screened by the underbrush, he turned and studied the river, to see on the water two equal bumps a hand's-breadth apart, with the long ripple behind that stood for "crocodile." But Crok smiled gleefully, made a gesture of contempt, and strode along his proper trail.

It was a hundred thousand years later when next I saw Crok. He was standing in that very same position by the edge of a dangerous stream, peering up and down for lurking foes, before making a dash for the other side. He saw his chance; and, dashing, reached an iron-bound isle in the middle.

Then again he looked about; and, seeing an opening, sped safely to the other shore.

Yes, it was Crok again. The alertness and vigor were there. The sinewy limbs were there, but hidden in broadcloth. The jaw might be a trifle less square, but the eye was even brighter. The broad young shoulders were masked in linen and fur, and short curls were where the unkempt thatch once hung. But it was Crok, descendant of the same old Crok; with Crockers, Crocketts and McCrockens for kinfolk.

But the river now was a *crowded street,* with roaring motor-cars and reckless drivers; the island in the stream was hedged with iron posts, and a policeman made it safer. But the dangers were as great, the need for speed and nerve.

The gifts that made Crok win a hundred thousand years ago are his to-day—and his the victory too.

THE WOLF AND THE MAN*

✒

A STORY-TELLER SHOULD ALWAYS TELL A STORY IN terms of his audience. He must talk the language that is vital to the people he addresses.

This means, when we take one of Andersen's charming tales, we must not merely translate it from Danish into English. We must go a little further and bring that English up to date, with the colorful touches that make it vivid in our own time.

This has been Seton's attitude in translating "The Wolf and the Man." A scholar, familiar with Danish as well as English, might object that, though keeping the main thought of the original, he has injected a hundred little ideas that find no place in the Danish. To which we reply: "Yes, he has; but by those very importations, he has given it vitality and rememberable force that it would not otherwise have had."

~~~~~

Long ago, all the animals lived in a big forest far from the haunts of man. They knew each other and how to deal with feuds among themselves, but man

---

*"The Wolf and the Man," from *Famous Animal Stories* by Ernest Thompson Seton, is reprinted here with the permission of Coward, McCann, publishers.

was little more than a tradition of some strange monster that few of them had even seen.

One day, the Fox and the Wolf were lying on a sunny bank, telling their adventures to each other. The Wolf was bragging of his strength, his speed, and his jaws. The Fox said contemptuously: "Of course, I have not got your great gifts. If it were not for a multitude of tricks that I have invented, I should stand a poor show. But I have learned that every creature has his weakness, and *that* weakness is *my* salvation. Why, even man with the far-killer is hard put to save his property when he and I have a show-down."

"Man! Who is man? What is man?" said the Wolf scornfully. "I only wish I could run across one. Are they good to eat?"

"Yes," said the Fox doubtfully. "I believe they are. But not for me. When I see a man, all I want is to get away, and go far and keep out of sight."

"Why," said the Wolf scornfully, "are they so swift?"

"No," said the Fox. "They are very slow."

"Are they strong?"

"Oh, no; not nearly so strong as you are, or the Bear."

"Have they sharp teeth and claws?" asked the Wolf.

"Why, no," said the Fox. "They have neither teeth nor claws."

"Well, what have they to be so terrible?"

"All I know," said the Fox, "is that they have magic, magic ways of learning about you, magic ways of harming you, magic ways of blighting you, without even touching you."

"Bah!" said the Wolf. "That's a lot of piffle. You have scared yourself with a bunch of old wives' tales. I only wish I had a chance for a try-out with one of those dreadful critters. Can you tell me where I can find one?"

"Yes," said the Fox. "I think I could find one for you. But I don't want to be in on the show-down. I will put you in touch with one, on condition that you give me a fair start so I can get clean away before things begin to happen."

"It's a bargain," said Isengrim.

"Come on then," said Reynard.

At a long fast trot, they set out away across the forest. They traveled all day and most of the night. Many a hill they climbed, many a stream they crossed, and early the next morning they emerged from the thick cover to an open country. From the top of a hill they had a fine view.

Then the Fox said: "You see far across the plain those curious flat, square-looking hillocks, some with stumps at one end, out of which comes what looks like mist?"

"Yes."

"Those are man-dens. You see, they nest in colonies, and generally out in open sunny places. I think if we sneak along close to their nesting places, we are sure to see one of the man-things."

The Wolf was delighted. He wanted to gallop openly and noisily on to the place. But the Fox said: "Please go slow. You promised you would give me a fair start before the mix-up."

"Yes," said the Wolf. "That is so."

So they went along cautiously, avoiding the places till they got within a short run of the man-dens. Then, by a well-worn pathway, they hid.

There was a good deal of noise, and they got glimpses of colored things in the thickets around the man-dens. "Those are the cubs playing," the Fox explained.

"It makes my mouth water," said the Wolf.

"Be quiet," said the Fox. "Look! Look! But lie low."

Along came one of the cubs walking on its hind legs, and whistling like a bird.

"Is that a man?" whispered the Wolf scornfully.

"No," said the Fox. "Not yet: but in a year or two, it will grow into a man."

So the man-cub passed. The Wolf could hardly keep from expressing his scorn of it.

The two animals waited some time, and along came a much bigger man-thing. Its body color was as red as the breast of a robin. It walked on its hind legs; one of the front legs was wholly gone, and one of the hind legs so thin that it looked like a stick. The man-thing seemed weak, for it went very slowly and dodderingly along.

"Is that a man?" asked the Wolf gruffly.

"Naw," said the Fox. "That used to be a man long ago. But it was all cut to pieces with fighting other man-things. Now it is nothing but a poor old has-been."

The Wolf grunted his disappointment.

After another long wait, the Fox crept up to the top of the bank; then at once dropped belly to ground and crawled back in some excitement.

"Here's one! A real one coming!" he gasped out.

And sure enough, here was a big, strong-looking, male man-thing striding along. His skin was loose in places and variously colored. He carried a big stick on one of his front feet, holding it over his shoulder. He had what looked like a cow's horn hanging by a long root about his neck. Around his body was a flat strip of bark, and in that, one or two bright shining sticks with crooks and knobs on them.

"Good," said the Wolf. And, giving a gurgle in his throat, he prepared to show off.

"Hold on," said the Fox. "You promised to wait till I was safely away."

"Don't you want to see the fun?" asked the Wolf.

"No," said the Fox. "I saw it once, and that was enough for me. All I want is a safe get-away."

"You poor, scared little simpleton," said the Wolf. "Run away if that's what you want to do."

"That's what I want to do," said the Fox. "Now,

please remember your promise. Don't start anything until you see my brush disappear over that distant hill." Then away he went like the wind.

The Wolf waited scornfully in hiding. The man-thing passed by. The Wolf made full notes of his make-up. He looked in vain for teeth or claws, and could not restrain his contempt.

Meanwhile, the Fox had cleared the far hill, and the Wolf was free to act. He raced after the man-thing, and as he drew near, he let off a deep war howl.

The man whirled about—and the fight was on.

The Fox had run fast and was far off by this time, but he heard some terrible roars and claps of thunder. He knew enough to get away while the gettin' was good, and for a moment deeply regretted his folly in going with the Wolf into Man-land. But the sounds ceased, and soon Reynard was safe once more in the thick cover of the forest.

Late the next day, while he was resting by the ford of the river, he heard a deep groan. With the true instinct of the hunter, he crouched in silence.

Then he heard another groan; and out of the forest, down the bank, crawled his old friend, Isengrim the Wolf.

But what a sorry spectacle! Bleeding, muddy, weak, and wounded, the Wolf crawled to the margin of the water and drank, long but feebly.

Reynard at once came forward, and said: "Good

Isengrim, you are ill. How is it? What can I do for you?"

"Oh, Reynard," said the Wolf. "I am sick. I am near dead. Do splash my head with water."

The Fox did what he could, and when the Wolf was somewhat refreshed and a little comforted, he told the story of his encounter with the man-thing.

"After you were well away, I went after the big man-thing. He had neither teeth nor claws, and he was so slow that I could run in circles around him. But—but—he had magic. He lowered his big crooked stick from his shoulder, and pointed it right at me. And in some way, he brought thunder and lightning out of the sky. The thunderbolt singed all the hair off my head, and the hail was so fierce that it bled my nose and put out an eye. This roused me to fury, and I sprang on him."

The effort of telling the tale nearly exhausted the poor Wolf.

"Oh, more water!" he gasped. Then when he was a little revived, he went on: "Oh, Reynard, I raced round to hamstring him as we do deer, but I could not find his hamstrings. So I leaped for his throat. But —but—he pulled out one of his own ribs, and slashed me with its keen edge and its sharp point. He cut my shoulder terribly, and so far I had not hurt him.

"I summoned up all my courage for another attack. But—but—but—he made more magic. He pulled out one of the little shining sticks that were tied to him with the bark strip. He pointed it at my face, and brought down more lightning out of the sky. It was a terrible thunderbolt. It blew off one of my ears, and left a long lightning track down my back. I felt I was licked, yet I wanted to die fighting. But he swung the long stick in his front paw and knocked me over the bank down into a deep ravine.

"Just at this, I heard one of the man-cubs screaming. Now, I thought, has come the whole pack to finish me. But it was good luck for me. The man-thing seemed to think another Wolf was after his cub. He left me to save the young one, and I was just able to crawl away.

"Oh, Reynard, I am terribly sick. Do take care of me. If you get me home, I'll be your friend for life."

Here the Wolf fainted.

But Reynard nursed him well. He got him home, and at last he recovered, except that henceforth he was lacking one eye and an ear.

He had, however, learned some wisdom. And, as he said to Reynard: "You were right. The man-thing is weak and slow, and has no teeth or claws. But it has magic. My strength can do nothing against that magic. Your wisdom is a better answer than my courage. I never again will face the man-thing."

THE STAG OF FONTAINEBLEAU

WHEN, SOME FIFTY YEARS AGO, SETON WAS AN ART
student in Paris, he often went with his friends to
one of the little inns that were found in the villages
on the border of the Great Forest of Fontainebleau.

The tap-room of the inn was the club-room of the
village, and every evening a jolly group of the local
peasantry assembled there to drink light wine and
exchange merry jokes and stories.

Seton spoke French fluently in those days and
found it amusing to join the good-natured groups.
Many of their stories were of adventures and ex-
ploits in poaching, in which occupation every man-
jack claimed to be active and successful. In fact, any
young gallant who was not a confirmed poacher
would have found little favor with the ladies of his
class; it meant he was what we could call "a sissy."

The game of the Great Forest was strictly preserved and was the property of one or two wealthy
families who paid to the State an annual rent for all
the shooting and hunting.

To hold these exclusive privileges, the patrician
owners had a well-drilled staff of competent game-
keepers, who patrolled the forest and its environs day
and night. These men were very loyal to their em-

ployers and never hesitated to act vigorously for game conservation.

Oftentimes the game-keepers, in conspicuous uniforms, would drop in for a friendly chat or a glass of wine. As soon as they entered, all poaching talk ceased. The old *braconniers* would shake their heads at Seton, wink, and lay their finger on the lips—a hint that he at once responded to.

One evening, after two of the game-keepers had called and gone off on their rounds, Seton pointed to a row of stag heads and horns all around the frieze of the tap-room and said: "How do you account for these?"

"Oh!" they said. "It is all right and lawful if we get them out on our crops or in our gardens."

"Well, why don't you bring them out? It ought to be easy at this time of year." For it was then October, the time when the stags were *en chasse*, that is, in rut.

The Frenchmen had never heard of such a thing, so Seton said: "Let's go out to-night and try."

Three or four student friends, the landlady, and her grown-up daughter said they wished to be in on it.

Staying at the *auberge* was a little Frenchman from the Boulevards of Paris. He said he was a sportsman. He always wore exaggerated sports togs, a cork helmet, a gun on his shoulder, and in his belt a revolver and a bowie knife. He had no hunting permit, but he was free to prowl along the highway and shoot a sparrow or two each day. These were duly cooked for him. He was known to the local people as "le Boulevardier."

As soon as the expedition was announced, he said, "I will not see the ladies go forth without a proper escort. I will go as their bodyguard. I would rather perish than have any ill befall them."

As nine o'clock drew near, on a dark and cloudy night, each of the *braconniers* began to have doubts. This one was tired, that one had to go home, so that none of them went with the Seton party. The company finally consisted of the two ladies, two art students, the Boulevardier and Seton.

To continue in Seton's words:

"As I passed by the crockery shelf, I reached up and secured a long cylindrical lamp chimney of glass, the well-known French type. I rumbled my voice through it, and said: 'That will do.'

"Then off we went under guidance of the landlady. She was a jolly woman in middle life, full of fun and droll speech.

"I said: 'Now it is up to you to take us to a part of the forest where we are sure to find stags.'

" 'That's easy,' she replied, and off we went into the dark forest, following the road with some difficulty.

"After half a mile's tramp, the gay lady said: 'Now, Monsieur Seton, do your stuff. There are always stags in this valley.'

"Remembering how my Indian friends—and sometimes I myself—used to decoy the big stags of Canada by use of a horn in the mating season, I raised the long lamp chimney, through it gave a couple of preliminary grunts, then a long deep bellow which was intensified by the hollow chimney. By swinging it in a figure-of-eight, I gave it the changing cadence of the stag's long challenge.

"The effect on our group was startling. They ceased their merry badinage; the English student said: 'Gosh!' Then all was still.

"I waited three or four minutes, then again vibrated the night air with another long challenge and several grunts.

"Not more than a few seconds passed when there was a response; from far up the dark valley it came.

"'*Grunt, grunt, grunt,*' then '*O-o-o-o-ah-ah-ah-ah-ho-o-o-o,*' the trumpet call of a royal stag *en chasse*.

"Now, for the first time, my companions believed that there was something in it. They were not only silent, they were a little awe-struck.

"After waiting a few minutes, I again gave my invitation to come and fight it out: '*O-oh o-ah o-ah ah-ah-ah-ah wo-o-o-o.*'

"This time, the response came from a couple of hundred yards away: '*O-o-o-wah O-o-o-wah.*'

"Then we heard the crashing of branches, showing that the stag was beating the bushes with his horns.

"The crashing was drawing nearer. Then there was stillness.

"I waited some time, then gave the raucous grunt that is the signal for charge.

"The answer came from the dark bushes only twenty yards ahead, and we knew the stag was rushing toward us.

"Fortunately we were in a grove of trees that had many limbs near the ground.

" 'Get the ladies up the trees,' I ordered.

"While this was being done, the dude said: 'I am sportsman. I have my revolvaire. I will die in defense of the ladies.'

"Then the landlady from her perch called out: 'Monsieur Sportsman, I think you better give that revolvaire to M. Seton.'

"So, unwillingly, the dude handed me the revolver, then shinned up a tree, right to the top.

"I could not see the stag, but he was grunting and crashing the brushwood some twenty-five feet ahead. I got down low on one knee hoping to see him against the sky. But I saw nothing. So I blazed away in the direction of the grunts, all six shots, without any effect—except to bring him on at me.

"I scrambled up the nearest tree. The big brute came out. He charged that tree and ripped the bark with his horns.

"Now I realized how foolish we had been, embarking on such an expedition at night, and unarmed.

"I said to my friends perched around me or nearby: 'Nothing for us now but to stay up here all night, and pray that it doesn't rain.'

"Suddenly, the dude cried out: 'I have found another cartridge.'

" 'Good luck. Let me have it.'

"I quickly put it in the revolver, cocked the weapon, took off my coat, then lowered the coat until it was in easy reach of the stag, and shook it tantalizingly against the trunk.

"The brute charged at it with all his fury, ground the coat up against the trunk and seemed intent on impaling it there.

"I lowered the revolver till it was just back of his ear—and fired.

"Down he went with a long grunt that dwindled away to nothing. Then all on the ground was still.

" 'Have any of you matches?' I asked.

" 'No. But,' said the dude, 'I have my cigarette-lighter.'

" 'Good! Let me have it.'

"I slipped down my tree. In a sheltered hole, I found some dry leaves, and soon made a fire.

"There was the stag—a stag royal—lying stone-dead.

"In haste and thankfulness, we turned toward home. The landlady was the first to recover her poise. She said:

" 'What are you all so sad about? Let's be joyful. I will sing for you.'

"We got back to the village about eleven o'clock. As we passed down the street, the jolly woman said:

'Give them a blast of your horn here. Stir them up. These people are all asleep.'

"I raised the echoes with my stag challenge, then we entered our abode.

"Next morning, we learned that half a dozen of the *braconniers* had heard the ringing calls and leaped out of bed to get the stag *en chasse* that had entered their village.

"In the afternoon, the landlady remarked casually to a game-keeper: 'I heard several shots in the Forest last night, near the swamp.'

"The game-keeper went to the place, guided partly by a couple of ravens, and found the carcase. He divided the meat with the landlord, and also gave him the antlers. I have often seen them since. They are the proudest ornament of the tap-room in the *auberge* where we hatched the plot."

ONATOGA'S SACRIFICE

WHEN MARQUETTE WENT DOWN THE MISSISSIPPI IN 1673, he saw on the rocky bluff where Alton, Illinois, now stands, the painting of a monstrous bird or dragon. It had horns like a deer, red eyes, and a beard like a goat; its body was covered with scales; it had wings and a very long tail which ended in a fish fin. The Illini told him it was the Piasa; and, by degrees, the story was pieced together. I give it as it came to me:

The red men had possessed all the great central part of the country, including the buffalo range, the valley ranges of the deer, and the high plains of the antelope. Game abounded, and the good hunters dwelt happily, for none were in want.

But, far to the north, was the great pine forest, the land of trees that never shed their leaves, the land of black rocks, long winter, and summer ice. This was the land of the Wendigo, of the Giants, of the Walker-on-the-Snow. The red men do not care to enter it; they are content to stay in the land of sun and plenty.

But Old Shingebis, who could hear the Voices and whose spirit could leave his body while he slept and go to far places, made report that in the black pineland were the Bird Serpents—monsters, red-eyed, horrible. They dwelt in caves and preyed on what they would, for not even Wendigo could face them in fight. "Piasani" he called them. He had seen them only in his dreams, by the power of his second sight.

Nevertheless, he knew him when, one day, there came a rumbling over the tree-tops. "The Piasa! The Piasa!" he cried.

The monster swooped down on the lodge of Piomatah and devoured him. After that, he came each day to seize and destroy, till that village of the Ojibwa was desolated. Then he went to the land of the Illini; and, at the first village, feasted as he would. So that, in one moon, its every lodge was empty.

Thus did the Piasa, till all the Illini west of the Little River were gone. The fear of death was on all, for none had strength to face the Piasa when he came, rumbling down from his dwelling-place in a cave by the big river.

Those were days of gloom and terror, and the great Chief Onatoga wept as he planned with Shingebis to gather the remnant of his people and take them to join their kinsmen east of the Great Lake, the Mishi Gumee.

But Shingebis said: "Make no move till I have fasted and prayed and harkened for the Voices."

So Shingebis went up into the hill which is called Wyanat, and fasted three days and three nights. There on the third night he heard the Voices, and this was the message that came:

"When you can find a perfect man whose heart has never been afraid, who has truly served his people without failing ever, who is willing to give his life to save them in this, their dire extremity, then may the Piasa be slain, and the people dwell again in peace and safety."

And the Voices put into the heart of Shingebis the strategem that would surely destroy the Terror. There were no words, but the vision was clear.

Shingebis returned to the village. There was heard the keening of the death wail, for three of their best warriors had been devoured by the monster, one each day.

The wise man hastened to the lodge of Onatoga. His face was painted black—he was mourning for his kin. He raised his hand in greeting.

Then Shingebis delivered the message that was given him. Onatoga heard him with keen attention.

Shingebis continued: "A perfect man who has never failed in warfare or in hunting, who has ever served his people without failure or thought of self."

The wise man paused, and gazed with searching eyes. There was silence for a time, then he went on:

"Onatoga, High Chief of the Illini, there is but one man perfect in our tribe. That man is you. Are you willing to die for them?"

"I am!" And the High Chief raised his head and forward reached his hand.

"Oh, Great Spirit, I rejoice in this. I am glad indeed to die in service of my people."

Then the wise man made clear the way that had been revealed.

"Twenty-four of our best archers must each make twelve new arrows. Each must go to the Sand Dunes where the rattlesnakes are found. Each must return with the venom of two rattlers; and with that, smear each arrow head. Each man must make and wear a head- and shoulder-dress of prairie grass. Then, by night, these, with Onatoga, shall march to the great river cliff where is the cave in which the Serpent Monster dwells, and call him forth to feast and die."

So, marching all night, these twenty-four brave bowmen, with the Chief and the Wise Man, came to the Great River, the Father of Waters. Across this was the high rock, with the dark place that meant the cave.

Crouching on the prairie, they slept, each man a bunch of prairie grass, twelve on this side, twelve on that. Between them was the Chief, and far behind him a buffalo skull.

When the sun arose, Onatoga stood up on a low hill, straight before the cave of the Piasa, and shouted aloud with all his might:

"Piasa, Piasa, Piasa!

"Come forth and eat!

"Here am I, Onatoga, Head Chief of the Illini!

"I am here to feed you with my flesh.

"Come and eat!

"Piasa, Piasa, Piasa!"

Then from the cave, there came a fearful rumbling

roar, and two great eyes of fire were seen in the gloom. Soon forth he came: "Rrrrrrrrrrr."

And Onatoga called again:

"Piasa, Piasa, Piasa!

"Come and eat.

"Here am I, ready to feed you.

"Come and eat."

Again the Piasa rumbled out his fearful cry. He spread his great dragon wings, sprang into air, and swiftly crossed the river, aiming straight for Onatoga who stood there, calm and undismayed, a willing sacrifice.

Over the prairie the monster sailed, and rumbled as he came.

He was within bowshot of the sacrifice, when up rose the twenty-four tussocks of prairie grass, each a bowman now, with deadly shafts. And twenty-four envenomed shafts flew true.

They reached the monster's heart; and as he fell, the speedy bowmen fired again.

Writhing, screaming in the agony of death, the winged serpent dropped not half a bowshot from the victim standing, waiting, unafraid.

The bowmen fired again. The Demon shivered, then, with a long, last, rasping groan, he trembled and lay still.

Suddenly up rose the buffalo skull that had lain still. Wearing that as a headgear came Old Shingebis, uttering his joy-cry as he came, the Zonzimondi of acclaim, the welcome to a hero coming home, the All-is-Well.

But Onatoga stood in doubt.

"I am here to die," he said.

"Nay," shouted Shingebis. "The Voices said: 'When a perfect man is found who is *willing* to die, then may the Piasa be slain.'"

And joyfully they chanted as they brought the hero home.

In the happy days of aftertime, the Illini brought their most skilled limners, and on the great flat face of the rock where he had dwelt, they made the portrait of the fearsome beast. There it is to this day. Some call it "Portrait of the Piasa," but many name it "Onatoga's Sacrifice."

LITTLE OTTO, THE CHARCOAL BURNER

LONG AGO, IN THE BLACK FOREST OF GERMANY, THERE was a charcoal burner named Little Otto. He had a dreadfully hard life. He had to work eighteen or twenty hours a day and seven days a week to make a bare living; so that, while yet in middle life, he was worn out with overwork and died in uncomplaining misery.

Now in the other world, he set out on the narrow pathway that led to the wicket gate which is the entry to heaven.

It so happened that the great Baron von Heimrod had died that same night in a drunken carouse. He also went tramping along the pathway and soon overtook Little Otto.

"Hello, who are you?" growled the Baron.

"Please, your honor, I am Little Otto, the charcoal burner from the Black Forest, and I am seeking for the side door to heaven." And he stood, hat in hand, to let the Baron pass.

"I am going that way, too," said the Baron. "So we will walk together."

Little Otto was overwhelmed with the condescension of the great Baron. He wanted to trot behind, but the Baron said:

"Oh, no. Up here it is different. We are more like equals."

So they came to the wicket gate. Otto hung back while the Baron beat a thundering summons with the knocker.

St. Peter came running in some alarm; it sounded as if the house was afire.

"Hello," said the Saint. "What would you?"

"This is heaven, isn't it?" grumbled the Baron.

"It's my office at the entrance to heaven," replied St. Peter.

"Well, I am the Baron von Heimrod, Black Forest of Germany, and I've come."

St. Peter took down the big ledger; and, running his finger down the H's, said: "Oh, yes, here you are. And who is this with you?"

Little Otto now came forward, and standing respectfully, bare-headed, said: "So please your reverence, I am Little Otto, the charcoal burner from the Black Forest of Germany."

St. Peter turned to the O's, and said: "Yes, yes. Here you are," and checked him off with a blue pencil.

The Saint turned to the Baron, and said: "Now, Baron von Heimrod, it won't take me long to get Little Otto placed, so, if you will excuse me, I'll attend to him first."

"Certainly, certainly!" replied the Baron. "We have all the time there is."

"Now, Little Otto," went on the Saint. "First I

must present you at court, and then we'll find out what you would most like to do."

"So please your reverence," said Little Otto, "I don't know anything about harps and crowns and choirs and things like that. No offense, your reverence, but if I could sit down in some quiet corner and have a good long loaf, that would suit me better than anything else. You see, I have never had a rest in my whole life."

"Certainly, certainly," rejoined the Saint. "But first I will introduce and announce you." This was soon done.

Then Little Otto went on: "Your reverence, if I could sit on the lowest step of the throne, away around that corner, then I could rest and see things without any one seeing me."

"Certainly, certainly," replied the Saint. "I'll come by and by, and see if you have everything you wish. If you should need me before I come, call one of those cherubs scooting around and send him to bring me."

"Oh, goodness, I wouldn't dare," exclaimed Little Otto.

"Pooh!" said St. Peter. "They are your servants. Don't be afraid."

St. Peter then hurried back to his office. He found the Baron walking up and down, rather impatiently, and twirling his mustache.

"Excuse me, Baron," said the Saint. "I was longer

than I expected. I had to explain things to your little friend."

"Oh, it's all right," said the Baron, "since you apologize. We'll say no more about it. After all, this is heaven."

"Now, what would you like to do?" asked St. Peter.

"Well," said the Baron, crossing his legs as he lolled back in a big chair, "you know, we Heimrods were rather a classy bunch, and hit a fast pace down below. We had a fine castle, a vast hunting range, a famous cellar, and entertained all the best people. And, really, I don't know of anything better that I could ask for. That is, the same things with certain annoyances left out, such as poachers, dishonest servants, and quarrelsome neighbors."

"Certainly, certainly," responded the Saint. "All these things will be properly attended to. There will be nothing to find fault with in those respects."

"Fine!" said the Baron. "Oh, by the way, there was one other disturbing element, not a small one. I was always in debt, always hard up. I never could keep my bank account right."

"Don't worry," said St. Peter. "You will find that your credit is unlimited. You will have no lack of cash. Now let's go and see it all."

So they stepped out the side door of the office, and came on a great highway. At that moment, up rolled a superb carriage with four horses, postilions, and flunkeys. On the panel were the Baron's arms and initials. The carriage stopped, the serving men leaped down and opened the door.

"Get in," said St. Peter.

"After you," replied the Baron. "You are now my guest."

So in they got and went spanking along the highway.

Soon they came to a beautiful archway with a hammered iron gate. On this the Baron's initials were set forth in decoration. Sentries flung wide the portal, showing a superb avenue of spreading elms and at the far end a gorgeous palace.

Every one was there to welcome the master to his home. There was a red velvet carpet on the steps, and rows of servants all in the Baron's livery.

They spent some hours going about, possessing, admiring. In the library there was a wonderful array of the best books.

"Very nifty," said the Baron. "I am not much for books myself, but some of my friends may use them. Anyway, it is the correct thing, and we Heimrods were always stylish."

Then they came to the billiard-room. On a side table were glasses, bottles, and drink. The Baron called to the butler standing near:

"Brandy and soda for St. Peter, and another for myself.

After a short time in the billiard-room, they took the elevator to the top of the castle, and, from a balcony, had a wonderful view. In the foreground were the stables, amply equipped, with plenty of thoroughbred horses. Beyond was a lake in the park, a lake swarming with fish. Far beyond was a range of wooded hills.

"See," said St. Peter, "as far as those hills and ten times as far, is the park alive with game, and it is all yours without a challenge, forever and ever. Now, is there anything else you would like?"

After a moment's hesitation, the Baron replied: "St. Peter, you have been so kind and generous that I am ashamed to ask. As a matter of fact, I am surprised at myself. But you asked me; and, if I am making a mistake, please don't put me in wrong with the authorities. You told me to ask for what I wanted. Well—well—couldn't you manage to run in a little harem on this otherwise perfect set-up?"

St. Peter smiled. "You don't suppose I've been running that office for two thousand years without learning something of human nature. You'll find a very complete harem in the left wing, and I can assure you that you will be pleased. Now I must go back to the office. There is probably a waiting line in it now."

So, after another brandy and soda, Peter bade the Baron good-by, and promised to call occasionally.

A thousand years went by, and all this time, St. Peter had no word from Little Otto, the charcoal burner. So he went in to see him one day.

There he was, just where the Saint had left him, on the lowest step of the throne, in a hidden corner, but with a broad grin of delight on his face. Oh, he looked so happy!

St. Peter went up to him and said: "Well, Little Otto, are you rested yet? Don't you want something else for a change?"

"Oh, thank you, St. Peter. I am nearly rested now. If I could have another spell as long as this one, I'd be just fine. I'd be ready to go the whole thing, harps and angels and everything. Why I am getting so pert, I spoke to an angel the other day."

"All right," said the Saint. "Any time you want me, send a cherub. Remember, he's your messenger-boy."

Now St. Peter always associated Little Otto with the Baron von Heimrod. So he decided to call on the latter also that day.

He found him sitting glum and silent in the billiard room, but he was not playing the game. A couple of winsome harem girls were hanging about, but the Baron was paying no heed to them. There were bottles and glasses on the table, but he was not drinking. He was gloomily staring at nothing when St. Peter came in.

"Morning," he said, dejectedly. "Sit down."

"Why, Baron," replied St. Peter, "you don't seem very cheerful."

"No," was the answer.

"Isn't the castle what you expected?"

"Yes."

"How about the hunting?"

"All right."

"Aren't the wines up to standard?"

"Yes."

"Are the ladies disappointing?"

"No."

"Well, what's wrong?" asked the Saint.

"See here now, St. Peter," responded the Baron in irritation. "The castle is all right, the cellar is fine, the hunting the best ever, the servants ideal, and the ladies most accommodating. But *it's always the same*, and I've just about come to the conclusion that this heavenly bliss isn't what it was cracked up to be."

St. Peter blew a couple rings from his cigar; then, turning to the Baron, he said: "Heavenly bliss! Where do you think you are?"

"Heaven, I suppose," drawled the Baron.

"Heaven!" exploded St. Peter. "No, you are in hell. What did you expect after the life you led on earth?"

"Hell?" shouted the Baron. "Well, this is very different from the hell I was told about."

"You'll find it is hell all right," replied St. Peter.

"H'mph!" said the Baron, with sudden composure. "Well, St. Peter, couldn't I have a different kind of hell for a change?"

"Certainly not!" thundered out St. Peter. "When you came in, I asked you what you wanted, and you proceeded to ask for every kind of selfish, carnal indulgence that your corrupted imagination could picture. I gave you everything you asked for, in fullest measure. And here you are in the midst of them, forever and ever. And you'll find out it is *hell* more and more."

"Interesting," said the Baron with a sneer. "I suppose there's nothing to do but make the best of it."

"That's all you can do," was the rejoinder.

Then, with a blaze of anger, the Baron retorted: "See here, St. Peter. I want you to understand that the von Heimrods never were quitters. We play the game and keep on smiling. If this is my lot for all eternity, I'll stay with it without grumbling, and make the most of it, and enjoy it, too."

"That's all you can do," was St. Peter's reply.

"By the way, St. Peter. You remember Little Otto who came in at the same time as I did?"

"Yes, indeed. I saw him a short time ago. Would you like to see him?"

"Why, yes. That would be a pleasant change," answered the Baron.

So they took the elevator to the top of the castle, then went along a narrow passage which led to a ladder, and that to a garret. There was a crack in the roof tiles, and St. Peter instructed: "There, look through."

The Baron looked, and realized that he was gazing into the great throne room of heaven, with angels, saints, and cherubs all about. And there, on the lowest step to the throne, in a quiet corner, was Little

Otto the charcoal burner, gazing about with a radiant happy countenance, a grin of intense joy on his face.

"Well, he's in heaven all right," said the Baron. "But, St. Peter, does he have to sit there forever and grin like that through all eternity?"

"No, indeed," replied St. Peter. "He could have a palace like yours and live a life of luxury, or he could go back on earth and meet his old pals and comfort them in their troubles. He has all the money he needs to help them, and all the power to cure their ills. And he can change as often as he wishes."

"Whew!" said the Baron. "That makes all the difference."

"All the difference," agreed the Saint.

"Well," said the Baron, "I won't squeal. Let's go down and have a brandy and soda."

After this, St. Peter said: "I must get back to the office."

"Good-by," said the Baron with a forced smile. "Come and see me when you can."

Another thousand years passed by, and St. Peter, on his rounds, called at the Baron's castle. But the servants were in trouble.

"We have searched everywhere and can find no trace of his Lordship, von Heimrod," they said. "We have gone through the stables, the woods, and even dragged the horse pond. But all in vain."

After some thought, St. Peter suddenly exclaimed: "I think I know."

He took the elevator to the top of the castle, climbed the ladder, and here in the garret, he found the great Baron on his knees, with his eyes eternally glued to that crack, gazing forever into heaven; surrounded by all the selfish pleasures his evil, bestial mind could conceive, gazing forever into the heaven of joy and peace, and suffering forevermore in a hell of ungratified desire.